Understanding the Science for Tomorrow: Myth and Reality

Jeffrey C. Grossman, Ph.D.

THE
GREAT
COURSES

PUBLISHED BY:

THE GREAT COURSES
Corporate Headquarters
4840 Westfields Boulevard, Suite 500
Chantilly, Virginia 20151-2299
Phone: 1-800-832-2412
Fax: 703-378-3819
www.thegreatcourses.com

MIX
Paper from
responsible sources
FSC® C011935

Jeffrey C. Grossman, Ph.D.

Professor, Department of Materials Science
and Engineering,
Massachusetts Institute of Technology

Professor Jeffrey C. Grossman is a Professor in the Department of Materials Science and Engineering at the Massachusetts Institute of Technology. He received his B.A. in Physics from Johns Hopkins University in 1991 and his M.S. in Physics from the University of Illinois at Urbana-Champaign in 1992. After receiving his Ph.D. in Physics in 1996 from the University of Illinois at Urbana-Champaign, he performed postdoctoral work at the University of California, Berkeley, and was 1 of 5 selected from 600 to be a Lawrence Fellow at the Lawrence Livermore National Laboratory. During his fellowship, he helped to establish their research program in nanotechnology and received both the Physics Directorate Outstanding Scientific Achievement Award and the Science and Technology Award.

Professor Grossman returned to UC Berkeley as director of a nanoscience center and head of the Computational Nanoscience research group, which he founded and which focuses on designing new materials for energy applications. He joined the MIT faculty in the summer of 2009 and leads a research group that develops and applies a wide range of theory and simulation techniques to understand, predict, and design novel materials with applications in energy conversion, energy storage, thermal transport, surface phenomena, and synthesis—working closely with experimental groups at each step.

Examples of Professor Grossman's current research include the development of new, rechargeable solar thermal fuels, which convert and store the Sun's energy as a transportable fuel that releases heat on demand; the design of nanoscale chords for ultrasensitive detection that could be used to sequence DNA in a matter of hours; 3-dimensional photovoltaic panels that when optimized deliver greatly enhanced power per area footprint of land; new materials that can convert waste heat directly into electricity; greener versions of one of the oldest and still most widely used building materials in the world, cement; nanomaterials for storing hydrogen safely and at high densities; and the design of a new type of solar cell made entirely out of a single element.

As a teacher, Professor Grossman promotes collaboration across disciplines to approach subject matter from multiple scientific perspectives. At UC Berkeley, he developed 2 original classes: an interdisciplinary course in modeling materials and a course on the business of nanotechnology, which combined a broad mix of graduate students carrying out cutting-edge nanoscience research with business students eager to seek out exciting venture opportunities. At MIT, he developed 2 new energy courses, taught both undergraduate and graduate electives, and currently teaches a core undergraduate course in thermodynamics.

To further promote collaboration, Professor Grossman has developed entirely new ways to encourage idea generation and creativity in interdisciplinary science. He invented speedstorming, a method of pair-wise idea generation that works similarly to a round-robin, speed-dating technique. Speedstorming combines an explicit purpose, time limits, and one-on-one encounters to create a setting where boundary-spanning opportunities can be recognized, ideas can be generated at a deep level of interdisciplinary specialty, and potential collaborators can be quickly assessed. By directly comparing speedstorming to brainstorming, Professor Grossman showed that ideas from speedstorming are more technically specialized and that speedstorming participants are better able to assess the collaborative potential of others. In test after test, greater innovation is produced in a shorter amount of time.

Professor Grossman is a strong believer that scientists should teach more broadly—for example, to younger age groups, to the general public, and to teachers of varying levels from grade school to high school to community college. To this end, he has seized upon a number of opportunities to perform outreach activities, including appearing on television shows and podcasts; lecturing at public forums such as the Exploratorium, the East Bay Science Cafe, and Boston's Museum of Science; developing new colloquia series with Berkeley City College; and speaking to local high school chemistry teachers about energy and nanotechnology.

The recipient of a Sloan Research Fellowship, Professor Grossman has published more than 90 scientific papers on the topics of solar photovoltaics, thermoelectrics, hydrogen storage, solar fuels, nanotechnology, and self-assembly. He has appeared on a number of television shows to discuss new materials for energy, including PBS's *Fred Friendly Seminars* and the *Ecopolis* program on the Discovery Channel's Science Channel. He holds 11 current or pending U.S. patents. ■

Table of Contents

Table of Contents

Table of Contents

Understanding the Science for Tomorrow: Myth and Reality

Scope:

In this course, we'll examine the ways advances in science and technology may change the fundamentals of the way we live in the future—what we eat and drink, how we travel, how we connect with each other, and even how long we live. Science operates through a rigorous process with lots of checks and balances, but there is plenty of room for creativity. In fact, coming up with creative ideas is one of the most important things a working scientist needs to do. We'll look at some of the most creative scientific ideas and technologies today in nanotechnology, computing, artificial intelligence, robotics, genetic engineering, neuroscience, renewable energy, and more. In each lecture, we'll examine the bedrock scientific principles that affect the direction that science of the future will take.

In order to separate fact from fiction, we first need to understand something about the way science works. The laws of nature don't change, of course, but our understanding of them does. With each new theoretical discovery, a multitude of new technologies comes into being—from computing to medicine. In turn, new technological devices make it possible to do new kinds of experiments, and the process begins again.

Our initial lecture dives into the scientific process itself, as we discuss how progress in science depends on a combination of creativity and careful scientific method. In subsequent lectures, we explore a host of different areas of scientific development.

We study the fundamentals of magnetism and new developments in electronics and spintronics and see how magnetism is used in medicine, transportation, and next-generation computing. Our examination of magnetic trains leads us to explore why there hasn't yet been the kind of revolution in transportation that we dream about in movies. We discuss the changes in energy production, storage, and conversion needed to make breakthroughs in transportation and even consider the possibility of virtual transportation.

Next, we discover how we got to a place where billions of transistors can cheaply be squeezed onto a single computer chip, how the exponential growth in computer power will finally come to an end, and what the next revolution in information technology might hold for us. We see why the quest for artificial intelligence has been so difficult—partly because of the serial way machines perform tasks and partly because we know so little about how we ourselves think. In our lecture on robotics, we see how robots can work for us and possibly someday with us.

We shed light on the power of seeing by taking a look at the incredible evolution—and revolution—in the technology of microscopes. The microscope is a perfect example of the way in which science and technology are intimately coupled: Advances in science have led to more powerful microscopes, which in turn allow us to carry out the next generation of science, which in turn leads to better microscopes, and so on. In fact, the invention of superpowerful microscopes helped launch the field of nanotechnology. We learn what exactly nanotechnology is and how and why it works with some detailed examples of how nanotechnology could revolutionize our world.

Then, we turn from materials science to biology. We see how advances in genetic engineering help us work with the key building blocks of life and even put them together from scratch, with applications from medicine to energy. We see how science is helping us understand the brain, even as technology is making strides in helping us interface with it. We study the life and death of cells and how scientists are working to enhance the cell's response to the challenges of cancer and aging. We learn that viruses are not all bad but may in the future serve as workhorses for medical cures, energy generation, and even the construction—atom by atom—of radically new materials.

Perhaps the single most important materials are the biological ones that we eat and drink. We take a look at changes science and technology make in what we eat and consider how food might be customized down to the smell, taste, and nutritional content. We learn how scarce potable water is becoming and consider new ways to produce and clean it in the future.

Then, we turn to topics related to energy. Fossil fuels and biofuels rely on the chemical processing of biological materials, but it takes nature millions of years to produce oil and gas. Growing our fuel seems like a good idea but might not make sense on a global scale unless we can use genetic engineering to optimize the energy of plants like algae or find new, cheaper ways of turning biomass into useable fuels.

We may find another energy solution by mimicking nature in capturing and harvesting the energy of the Sun. Solar cells can capture the Sun's energy and convert it directly into electricity, although at an expense that is far greater than essentially all other renewable energy technologies. We learn why this is the case and how advances in the science and technology of this fundamental photon-to-electron conversion process are leading to completely new materials—even plastics—that can perform the conversion much less expensively.

Moving on from energy conversion to energy storage, we talk about batteries: how it is possible to make chemicals store electrical energy, why there's been such a slow improvement in the technology over time, and what the future holds. We learn about the hydrogen economy and why using hydrogen, the simplest element known, as our carrier of energy faces crucial challenges, including how it is generated and how it is stored. We see why nuclear power is still such an appealing dream, even though it has fallen far short of hopes in the past.

As we move to the end of the course, we discuss the science of prediction and consider why it can be so hard to make accurate predictions about complex systems—from stock markets to the weather. In our lecture on communication, we review dramatic changes in the way we share information and consider the likely evolution of communication in the future. We conclude the series by talking again about how science progresses, how it relates to our culture, and what lies ahead.

Science never stops changing. That's the beauty of it. ■

Changing the Game
Lecture 1

In this course, we'll look at the ways science and technology may change the fundamentals of the way we live: what we eat and drink, how we travel, how we learn, how we communicate with each other, and even how long we live. In order to separate fact from fiction, we first need to understand the way science works. Throughout the course, we'll highlight myths as well as misconceptions. Myths tend to solidify and remain unchanged over time to the point where they become irrelevant. Science, on the other hand, never stops advancing—that's the beauty of it.

The Game of Science

- Science operates through a rigorous process with many checks and balances—but there's also plenty of room for creativity. In fact, coming up with creative ideas is one of the most important things a working scientist needs to do.

- It may be helpful to think of science as a game. Like any game, science has a very well-defined set of rules. It's just like checkers or chess—only particular moves are allowed. If we don't follow these rules, then we are cheating at the game, and most importantly, we don't have much chance of achieving our goal and "winning" the game.

- For science, the goal is to enhance and improve human knowledge of nature. The game is called the **scientific method**. In this method, we begin by asking a question: Why are leaves green? Then, we look up everything we can that's related to the question at hand— for example, how trees grow and what makes color.

- At that point, we can construct a hypothesis to try to answer our original question. Sometimes the hypothesis is little more than an educated guess while other times it is based on a complex deduction;

either way, the next part of the game is to test the hypothesis by carrying out an experiment.

- If your hypothesis turned out to be true, then you would report your results. Now, this does not necessarily mean that you've found the correct answer but, rather, that given your data, you have shown that your hypothesis could be correct. Then, further experiments are conducted, and other scientists repeat or expand on your original question.

- Sometimes an experiment cannot give a conclusive answer simply because the scientist didn't have the right tools to perform it. In an effort to obtain a more accurate answer, technology steps in to develop new tools—ones that improve crucial aspects of the experiment.

- New tools drive new technologies, which in turn lead to new scientific understanding, which further drives technology. Of course, though, technology isn't limited to serving only science.

- The rules and checks and balances laid out by the scientific method are not only designed to keep us honest; those checks and balances are also what stimulate us to refine our ideas and to continually ask new questions.

Playing the Game

- A complete understanding of the real cause and effect enabled by science allows for technological progress to be made. New opportunities arise as well as new challenges—some of them unpredicted—and the game starts all over again.

- Even in modern science, sometimes we have data that we don't want to recognize at first because we don't understand what mechanism of action could account for it, but these are often the very things that lead to great scientific advances.

- In fact, many of the scientific advances over the last several centuries were initially regarded as controversial by the general public and often by fellow scientists as well.

- When quantum mechanics was proposed, for example, many were skeptical. The idea that a particle—or any object, really—could behave as a wave was considered almost insane, but that very same idea and the theory as we now know it is the foundation of much of the technology we make and use today.

- As in any game, a referee is required. The final step in the scientific method is to write up your experiment in a report, describing your ideas and what methods you used to test them. The report is then sometimes presented to peers at conferences and published in journals. This results in feedback and discussion of

The theory of relativity, formulated by Albert Einstein (1979–1955), would not have been possible without the laws of mechanics that came before it.

the findings, which then leads to further experimentation along with new questions, experiments, or hypotheses.

- Of course, progress is only made possible by the work done by others before us. For example, Einstein's theory of relativity—which combines and explains the fabric of space and time as woven together—wouldn't have been possible without Newton's analytical laws of mechanics. These laws were in turn not possible without Galileo's formulation of the laws of motion.

- The literature is the starting point for any scientist who wants to know what the level of development in his or her field is. As scientists, we know we can rely on the literature because it was the result of the same game we are playing today—with the same rules.

- Does this mean we should not question these results? Of course not. After all, science is all about asking new questions. However, such questioning should always follow the rules of the game.

Myths within the Game

- At the heart of homeopathic medicine is the conjecture that water retains a memory of the substances that were once dissolved in it to some specific dilution. Scientists claimed to have found proof of it. Following the scientific method, they submitted their work for publication.

- If you submit a piece of work to a scientific journal, it will be reviewed in great detail, especially for topics so potentially revolutionary. When reviewers asked to have some of the water memory experiments repeated, nothing definitive could be proven, and the paper was rejected.

- In this specific case, the experiments that were done were not analyzed correctly, and the results were used only to justify an assumption. Sometimes scientists will make assumptions and look for any possible way to make them believable. This is what happened during the water memory debacle.

- Even though homeopathy today is very well known and widespread, there is not a single scientific experiment that has ever been done to validate its benefits. This doesn't mean that homeopathy won't in some cases cure someone, but the cure is most likely a placebo effect, which is a very well-established clinical and scientific theory.

- Therefore, we can safely categorize the memory of water and homeopathy as myths—not science. As we can see in the water memory example, if a myth is persistent enough, it can eventually develop into a **pseudoscience**, which is only masquerading as science.

- The pseudoscience that is probably the best known is astrology. Pseudosciences often mimic real science: They have theories, they make predictions, they perform measurements, they analyze data, and their experts make presentations to peers.

- The difference is that pseudosciences rest on assumptions that simply cannot be proven. For example, looking at the success rate of an astrological prediction, you will find that the chances that the prediction is correct are essentially the same as pure coincidence.

- This is the problem with confusing pseudoscience with science. Predicting with scientific accuracy means that one can go back to the predictions you made and know that they were correct, at least to some extent.

- Because of the disconnect with reality, a myth or pseudoscience is not likely to translate into scientific progress, but that doesn't mean that a myth is always a bad thing. As long as the boundaries between myth and science are well defined, the 2 can—and, in fact, do—go hand in hand.

- Many of our modern gadgets were "predicted" by popular culture 50 years ago; cell phones, personal computing, e-commerce, plasma televisions, and MRIs are a few examples.

- Still others, like the teleportation in *Star Trek* or the flying cars of *The Jetsons*, are still science fiction—at least for now. These 2 examples both have to do with transportation, which has suffered from the fact that an energy revolution similar to the information revolution has not yet occurred.

- Sometimes myths are a way to express a vision for the future that is often based on an unrealistic extension of a scientific or technological theory. This can be mere wishful thinking, of course, but sometimes a myth can serve as motivation and inspiration. A major leap in scientific advancement is what is required to get there.

- Sometimes even good science can produce a fantasy that is never fulfilled—not because of a lack of scientific merit, but for other social, economical, or environmental reasons.

Science and the Future

- Science and technology are closely interconnected with each other because the evolution of one relies on the parallel evolution of the other. Through scientific discovery and understanding of how nature works, we find new ways to mimic nature or improve upon it. This is technology's role, but it also enables new science to be accomplished.

- For millennia, science has given us knowledge of how the world works that led in turn to more magnificent discoveries and extraordinary innovation. As a result, we enjoy higher standards of living (and live much longer and healthier), have a greater appreciation for the wonders of our universe, and can be inspired in new ways that challenge and extend our imaginations. And, yet, rarely—if ever—has there existed an absolute need for science as there exists today.

- The problems we face now are global in nature, not local. The problems we face now will have long-term consequences, not short term. The problems we face now threaten our entire way of life and indeed life itself, not just a small part of our lives. The problems we face now have an urgency to them we cannot afford to test.

- This is a pivotal moment in time for science, a moment when—if strongly supported by our government, our industries, our investors, and our people—science research can solve these problems, meet the challenges we face head-on, and fundamentally change the world.

pseudoscience: A myth that is persistent enough to masquerade as science.

scientific method: A cyclic process of inquiry based on observations, synthesis, hypothesis, and predictions that lead to more observations.

Suggested Reading

Carey, *A Beginner's Guide to Scientific Method*.

Franklin, *What Science Knows*.

Questions to Consider

1. What makes science different from myth?

2. If you wanted to perform a science experiment, what rules and processes should you follow?

Magnetism—The Science of Attractions
Lecture 2

In this lecture, we will define magnetism—which is all about attraction and anti-attraction, or repulsion—and discuss some exciting examples of the promise of new technologies based on the science of magnetism. Magnetism is enormously important in the world today, with applications ranging from electric motors to compasses and from inductive heating to information storing. In the future, magnetism will be even more important, enabling revolutionary technologies from levitating transportation to medical device breakthroughs to a new era of computing.

Magnetism

- A **magnet**, very broadly, is any material that produces a magnetic field. Then, if we bring certain other materials near that field, they can "feel" it. This is what we mean by **magnetism**—it's the effect of a magnetic field created by a magnet on another material.

- Magnetism was discovered thousands of years ago because there are naturally occurring magnets that exist in certain rocks in the ground that produce these fields.

- A magnet is simply an object with 2 poles that are attracted to each other. One of these poles is called the north pole, and the other is called the south pole. Every magnet has 2 poles—from the horseshoe magnet to the needle in a compass to the planet Earth itself.

- A magnet can never have just one pole. If you were to take a magnet with its north and south ends and cut it down the middle, the 2 pieces would each have their own north and south ends—just as the original larger piece had a north and south end.

- One of the simplest ways to "see" the field of a magnet is to take a magnetic bar with its north and south poles and sprinkle something that feels the pull of the field—for example, small particles of iron. What you'll see is that the tiny particles will be pulled into conformity with the field lines, called lines of force, which act on magnetic materials like iron.

- Magnetism has the same origin in all magnets. In fact, even one of the smallest objects we know of is itself a magnet with 2 poles: the electron, which sits around just about every atom and forms the basis for all bonding between atoms.

Magnetism and Electricity
- A magnetic field is created any time there is an electric charge rotating in a circle. This is tells us that electricity and magnetism are intimately related to each other—something that James Clerk Maxwell helped to formalize with his very famous set of equations hundreds of years ago.

- Earth itself is a very big magnet. The core of Earth is made of iron, is molten, and, very importantly, has electronic charges throughout. The core rotates because of Earth's rotation, so the electric charge is moving in a circle, which creates a magnetic field.

- Earth's magnetic field is always there—as long as Earth is spinning—and it's what a compass responds to. In a compass, there is a small piece of magnetic material that feels those force lines from the magnetic field of the planet, and it tries to align with the lines. A compass will always point north or south because, no matter where you are, the field lines wrap around from the North Pole to the South Pole of the planet.

- Because of the fact that moving charge creates magnetism, we can also make artificial magnetic fields at any time simply by running a current through a metal wire. We can also do the opposite: By driving a magnet into a coiled up electric wire, we can produce a current.

- The process of heating by induction has been known and used for nearly a century and has been utilized heavily in various manufacturing processes. It involves running an alternating current through a coil, producing a magnetic field. The advantage of induction heating is that there is no flame and no contact with a heat source.

- If the coil that generates the magnetic field is lined up with another coil of the same shape, then the electricity can be directed into a battery instead of being used to heat a material up. This is what is behind the concept of wireless charging.

- The technologies behind inductive charging and heating are still being optimized and improved, but because of the many benefits of inductive energy transfer, we can most definitely expect to see much more of it in the near future.

Magnetism and Electrons

- An atom has tiny charges around it—which are the electrons—so an atom all by itself can be a magnet. We can exploit the magnetic properties of an individual atom through nuclear magnetic resonance (NMR) and magnetic resonance imaging (MRI).

- NMR works in the same way as a wireless charger, but instead of being used to charge a phone, the magnetic field is used to probe the inner workings of a molecule. What makes this happen is the particular response of a material (in this case, the molecules in your body) to the field lines of a magnet.

- Some materials can be permanently magnetic, and the reason has to do with their atomic structure. **Ferromagnetic** materials are examples of materials that can be permanently magnetized. Within them are small domains where all of the atoms have their tiny magnets pointing in the same direction.

- There are some naturally occurring permanent magnets—such as the mineral lodestone, or magnetite. However, most permanent magnets are not truly permanent; instead, they start out with their tiny domains pointing their magnetic north and south poles in random directions but then can be aligned by applying an external field.

- One application of permanent magnets is the hard drive. Basically, a hard drive is a thin sheet of magnetic material, often a cobalt-based alloy, in which we can control the tiny magnetic domains to see which way their north and south fields are pointing (reading) or to apply a magnetic field to switch the direction they are pointing (writing).

- In a hard drive, we magnetize tiny domains within the large sheet. Then, the hard drive quickly writes or reads these tiny domains, which are made to point their magnetic fields either up or down—corresponding to the natural language of computers, 1s and 0s. Because the domains are so small, we can store trillions of those tiny bits of information on a single sheet.

- An important related technology advance is known as giant magnetoresistance, the discovery for which the Nobel Prize was awarded in 2007. Magnetoresistance takes advantage of the effect that magnetic properties can have on electronic properties by layering ferromagnetic materials with nonmagnetic materials.

The Future of Magnetism
- In the future, there could be some very interesting applications in information technology—what we might call magnetronics, or as it is usually referred to in the scientific arenas, **spintronics**.

- In fact, the discovery of giant magnetoresistance is credited with giving birth to the field of spintronics. At the heart of spintronics is the fact that even just a single electron is a magnet, with its very own magnetic north and south poles.

- Today, there isn't anything like electronics that instead uses magnetism, but we could hypothetically use the spin of the electron in place of the charge of the electron to do computing. In this way, spintronics could be the future of electronics. Since no electric current is needed, there is no major power consumption involved in such spin operations.

- In addition to the advantage of low power use, the spin of an electron can change in a much faster way than flipping an electric switch in an electronic circuit, so the computing speeds could be substantially faster.

A technology that is based on magnetism, an alternator is the electric motor that cranks up a car to get it started.

Types of Magnetic Materials

- Most materials cannot be permanently magnetized. If a material does not contain those tiny magnetic domains, then the material doesn't allow the atomic magnetic fields to stay all aligned in any particular direction— even if we apply a strong magnetic field. These materials are called **paramagnetic**.

- While still not having magnetic domains, **diamagnetic** materials react to an applied external field with an internal field in the opposite direction. Therefore, if we place a diamagnet on top of a permanent magnet, the former will float on top of the latter because the diamagnet's opposing field causes the 2 to repel.

- One example of a diamagnetic material is water. Its diamagnetic response to an applied external magnetic field is not very strong, but it is still strong enough to feel repulsion when placed near a strong enough magnet.

- Because animals have a considerable amount of water in them, then this effect should be able to make a live animal levitate. In fact, we have actually been able to float a live frog by levitating it above a very powerful magnet.

- However, we're probably not going to be levitating a person in this way any time soon because the magnet required would be too large, and it's also not known whether there could be adverse health risks from such a large field.

- **Superconductors** are similar to diamagnets in the sense that in the presence of an external field, they respond with a field of their own in the opposite direction. However, superconductors have essentially no resistance to electrical conduction, so you could run a current through a superconducting wire and it would, in principle, continue forever without diminishing.

Applications of Magnetic Fields

- Maglev trains are one of the most interesting applications of diamagnetic properties. Using the diamagnetic properties of superconductors, and the fact that there is very little electrical dissipation due to the superconductivity, maglev trains would be able to provide the necessary magnetic fields with little power required.

- Maglev trains could, in principle, provide a cost-effective way toward levitating transportation. However, superconductors today require extremely low temperatures, are not cheap to make, and require fairly complex manufacturing processes.

- Scientists are working on these problems, and enormous progress will continue to be made. Superconductors today can run at much hotter temperatures than those of just 30 years ago, but it still takes $-140°C$ to make them work. Prototype maglev train lines have already been built.

- With levitating transportation, there's no noise and no friction between the track and the train, so the efficiency of energy used to make the train move forward is much higher. In addition, maglev transportation can be used as a platform for other future transportation ideas.

- Using magnetic fields to levitate an object can be applied anywhere that low friction and low drag are needed. For example, bearings with low friction can provide a significant improvement in battery life by lowering power consumption in an electric motor. There would also be no need for lubrication because there are no mechanical parts rubbing against one another.

Important Terms

diamagnetic: Materials that do not have magnetic domains and react to an applied external field with an internal field in the opposite direction.

ferromagnetic: Materials that can be permanently magnetic because of their atomic structure.

magnet: Very broadly, any material that produces a magnetic field. A magnet is simply an object with 2 poles that are attracted to each other. One of these poles is called the north pole, and the other is called the south pole.

magnetism: The effect of a magnetic field created by a magnet on another material.

paramagnetic: Materials that cannot be permanently magnetic because of their atomic structure.

spintronics: Similar to the field of electronics that instead uses magnetism and that hypothetically uses the spin of the electron in place of the charge of the electron to do computing. At the heart of spintronics is the fact that even just a single electron is a magnet, with its very own magnetic north and south poles.

superconductor: A material that, at sufficiently low temperature, exhibits zero resistance to the flow of electric current. Like diamagnets, they react to an applied external field with an internal field in the opposite direction.

Suggested Reading

Matricon, Waysand, and Glashausser, *The Cold Wars*.

Moon, *Superconducting Levitation*.

Shinjo, *Nanomagnetism and Spintronics*.

Tinkham, *Introduction to Superconductivity*.

Questions to Consider

1. Explain why electric motors should really be called "magnetic motors." How do they work?

2. When we talk about magnetism, why do we often say that everything is spinning? What's spinning, and what does it do?

Transportation—The Science of How We Move
Lecture 3

All of the technological advances that have allowed various modes of transportation to travel farther and faster have created many expectations for the realm of transportation. Some of the more popular ones that have surfaced over the past 50 years have been flying cars, jet-propulsion cars, intercontinental supersonic jets, space vehicles, cars based on portable nuclear power plants, and levitating trains. Of course, some of these expectations were made into realities, and some were not. Regardless, at the heart of every means of transportation is energy source and efficiency of use.

The History of Transportation

- **Transportation** is the act of moving people or things from one place to another place. The first role that science played in transportation was to simply recognize our own physical limitations.

- The first step we took to move beyond the limitations of our own bodies was to use animal power. Using oxen improved our transportation of heavy equipment for agriculture. Using horses improved our transportation of people and goods.

- The first real technological advance came when we started to use engineering to create new methods for moving around. The wheel is just such an advance. Invented many thousands of years ago, the wheel has had an enormous role in transportation.

- Science and technology can bring important new advances but also create new problems as a result. For example, the widespread use of horses created enormous environmental and health issues related to the exhaust of the horses themselves. Those same exhaust problems exist in most transportation technologies that we have today.

- When using batteries, there are no emissions from the vehicle itself, but we still need to make energy in order to charge the battery, so there's still pollution in generating that electricity. However, the energy is stored cleanly, which allows us to possibly get the energy from renewable resources.

Nuclear-Powered Transportation
- In 1958, Ford unveiled a model nuclear-powered car called the Nucleon. In this car, a miniature nuclear fission reactor would hypothetically sit in the back, giving off enough heat to boil water to power the car with a steam engine. Given that nuclear fuel could last for a decade or more, the dream was that the fuel for cars would simply be water, and it would have no emissions.

- The kind of nuclear power we know how to make today carries far too many challenges to be utilized in this way, especially from an environmental and safety standpoint. However, even if those problems had been solved, there was another technological hurdle: the miniaturization of nuclear power to the point that it would fit in a car.

- In the 1950s, nuclear energy was being explored for just about every other means of transportation. For example, rockets used for deep-space exploration have been powered by nuclear energy.

- While we've seen the nuclear car appear in a few video games and a few Hollywood movies, that's probably where the vision of the nucleon will remain.

Electrically Powered Transportation
- The electric motor was available before the internal combustion engine by nearly 30 years, and it was known to be more efficient and cleaner. However, gas became the preferred choice because it has a much higher energy density than batteries. Therefore, the range of transportation was much greater, and gasoline-powered cars were more economically viable.

- The electric engine has been available for about 180 years, but the problem was in the amount of energy that could be stored electrically. The key advances have been to increase the density enough to make electric cars at least somewhat competitive with traditional ones.

- Batteries are still quite expensive, and they still don't have the same range as a gas tank in a typical car. However, the trade-off between range and cost—and being much more environmentally friendly—is pointing quite strongly toward a future that returns to a concept of the past, one filled with electric vehicles.

The problem in making electric engines prevalent has been in the amount of energy that can be stored electrically.

- There are essentially 3 types of electric vehicles on the market today. The first is the electric-gasoline hybrid, which was first brought to market in the Toyota Prius. In a hybrid vehicle, the battery is quite small; it can store only about 1 or 2 kilowatt-hours of energy.

- A watt is a unit of power, measured in joules per second, and a joule is a unit of energy. A kilowatt-hour can provide 1000 joules of energy per second continuously for an hour. A gallon of gasoline stores about 36 kilowatt-hours of energy. The battery in a hybrid, with its 1 or 2 kilowatt-hours, stores very little energy by comparison.

- Gasoline-powered engines are not very efficient. Less than 25% of the energy in a gallon of gas is used to actually make a car move. The rest is completely wasted, mostly as heat. Electric cars use as much as 90% of the energy in their batteries to make the car move—3 to 4 times as efficient as gasoline-powered engines.

- The other 2 kinds of electric vehicles are just starting to appear on the roads; they're known as plug-in hybrids and all-electric cars. Both have much larger batteries: Around 15 kilowatt-hour batteries are used in plug-in hybrids, and between 25 and 50 kilowatt-hour batteries are used in all-electric cars.

- The plug-in hybrid, brought first to market in the Chevy Volt, is basically an electric car that runs on a battery. The motor is electric and, therefore, highly efficient—unlike in the lighter hybrids. In a plug-in hybrid, there's also a gas tank that can be used to generate electricity for the battery once it runs out.

- In all-electric cars, such as the Nissan Leaf, a bigger battery is used so that the range of the car driving on only the battery can be as much as 100 miles. However, in an all-electric car, there's no backup; when the energy in the battery runs out, the car won't go until you can plug it in.

- These 2 electric-car technologies will likely compete against one another for many years to come. We don't know which one will win, but we do know that the future of road transportation is almost certainly electric.

Transportation in the Air
- A jet-engine plane can carry a lot more passengers than a small turboprop plane, and if it's full, it's almost as efficient. However, if you could only fill 50 seats out of the 416 that a 747 jet can hold, then the efficiency goes so far down that it becomes economically unviable—which is why airlines have a general policy of overbooking flights.

- It all comes down to how much energy it takes to lift a certain amount of weight and whether that efficiency is viable or not. That's why some birds can't fly, even though they have wings.

- In his **square-cube law**, Galileo described the principle that if you increase the size of an animal, for example, by a factor of 2, then you're increasing its area by a factor of 4 and its volume by a factor of 8.

- The lift of a bird's wing is proportional to the area of the wing. For a bird that's twice as big, its wing area increases by a factor of 4, which means it would have 4 times as much lift. However, because the volume is 8 times larger, so is its mass. As a result, it only has 4 times as much power but needs to lift 8 times as much weight.

In the future, increasing the speed of turboprop planes will require propellers with different designs and made from new materials.

- Our goal isn't only to try to increase the weight of the objects we can fly around. We also care about speed. For one thing, it takes more fuel to go faster, and going faster also means noisier and with more emissions—neither of which scale linearly with speed. In addition, cost does not scale linearly with speed; we've had supersonic air travel for decades now, but very few people can afford it.

- Scientists are seeking to reduce costs, emissions, and noise by turning back to something that looks like the very first airplanes—namely, turboprops. They are slower, but they can be made to be more efficient than jet engines and are also less polluting.

- One of the challenges we'll need to tackle is how to increase the capacity of turboprops to make them larger than they are today. Going beyond today's capabilities in terms of speed for a turboprop plane will require propellers with different designs that are made from new materials.

- There are many other kinds of flying machines, including helicopters, gliders, and planes that can take off vertically. For many decades, we've dreamt of flying around at speeds much faster than cars and using routes that are much more direct—and with less traffic—than roads.

- The concept of portable jetpacks has been an enormous challenge to turn into a reality, mainly because of the square-cube law combined with how much power is in our fuels. Nevertheless, commercial jetpacks—at $75,000 each—are starting to emerge that can only run for about 30 minutes on a tank of gas. The technology is now good enough to put many more of these in the skies soon.

A Transportation Revolution

- Compared to other technical revolutions, such as information technology, transportation has evolved at a much slower pace and is still using all of the same basic paradigms from a century ago—such as fossil fuels and internal combustion engines.

- The key challenge of today's transportation lies in improving overall efficiency without limiting range and possibly speed. Improved efficiency will ultimately result in a lower cost per mile per passenger, but a revolution in energy storage and production is needed.

- Transportation has, in fact, changed quite considerably from a century ago. Other revolutions in electronics, for example, have brought us a much improved, cleaner way to burn fuel, a safer design for our cars, and a smarter, more efficient way to locate places.

- In addition, biotechnology will bring major advances. Artificial fuels based on much cleaner technologies could be used in place of fossil fuels, reducing our carbon footprint and the emissions of toxic chemicals.

- Advances in artificial photosynthesis may ultimately jump-start a new revolution in transportation, scrapping carbon-based fuels in favor of more sophisticated ways to convert renewable resources directly into motion.

- In addition, new materials based on nanotechnology will enable the design of much lighter airplanes and cars as well as even better roads. Lighter means of transportation will require a lot less power to move and, therefore, lighter and more efficient engines, leading to an overall improvement in efficiency.

- The biggest contribution to revolutionize transportation is going to be in energy production, storage, and conversion. However, the revolution would not be complete if it didn't also involve the transportation infrastructure itself: the roads, stations, and ways of distributing energy.

- Scientists are already starting to work on radical new concepts, but more scientific solutions are needed in energy production and storage and in the distribution of the energy.

- Part of any revolution in transportation will also involve much more intelligent vehicles. The ability of moving vehicles to communicate their exact locations and speeds with one another and to either make or suggest decisions to the driver will be something that is naturally built in to our transportation of the future.

- New capabilities regarding the amount of digital information that can be exchanged every day may ultimately mean a significant reduction in the needs of conventional transportation. The age of virtual transportation is already a reality in video games, and such virtual interactions will have important impacts on how we use transportation in the future and possibly will redefine the meaning of transportation itself.

Important Terms

square-cube law: In this law, Galileo described the principle that if you increase the size of an animal, for example, by a factor of 2, then you're increasing its area by a factor of 4 and its volume by a factor of 8.

transportation: The act of moving people or things from one place to another place.

Suggested Reading

Blatner, *The Flying Book*.

Darling, *Teleportation*.

Lay, *Ways of the World*.

Sperling and Gordon, *Two Billion Cars*.

Zeilinger, *Dance of the Photons*.

Questions to Consider

1. What has prevented us from having the transportation revolution we once imagined, such as the flying cars from *The Jetsons*?

2. Why don't elephants fly?

Computers—Trillions of Bits per Second
Lecture 4

Computing is a technology that became 20 times more powerful in just 10 years and 20,000 times more powerful in 30 years. In addition, while growing exponentially more powerful, it also became less expensive. Furthermore, this technology has changed basically every single way in which we live—from how we work, to how we drive, to how we shop, to how we communicate, to how we cure diseases, to enabling us to put people on the Moon. Computing is the one technology that has accomplished all of this in our history.

The History of Computing

- It wasn't until the 1930s that the first real thinking went into the possibility of calculating machines that could add and subtract and carry out perhaps even more complex math operations.

- Before the 1940s, there were many small devices that were based on mechanically moving parts and were used to compute specific functions, dating all the way back to the ancient Egyptians.

- Although there are many different designs for mechanical computers, the basic idea is the same: a set of wheels with notches or teeth in them, each one representing a digit. As they rotate, if they go past a full turn, they can make the wheel next to them turn through sophisticated gears.

- The history of mechanical computing in its essence is the story of the numeral wheel and the devices that rotate it to register numbers 0–9 and carryover values in 10s.

- The first large mechanical computers were built in the 1940s. Built in 1944 at Harvard University, the Mark 1 was an electromechanical computer, which means it was still based on mechanical switches but used electric motors to do the switching.

- In 1946, a groundbreaking advance was developed: ENIAC (Electronic Numerical Integrator and Computer) was built at the University of Pennsylvania. It is considered to be the first general-purpose, all-electronic computer.

- In its time, ENIAC was an impressive computing machine: It could do 357 multiplications or 35 divisions per second, making it immensely faster than Mark 1. It wasn't just its speed that made ENIAC so special; it was also its flexibility.

- Analog computers used combinations of measured data, such as the voltage or currents in an electronic circuit or the frequency of a wave from a sound vibration.

- Digital information, on the other hand, uses variables that are either on or off—like a 1 or a 0. Any information can be represented digitally—for example, an audio wave for music can be sampled digitally and converted into a large set of 1s and 0s.

- Digital signals can be converted to analog, and vice versa. Most computers today are digital because it leads to much more precise control in calculations. ENIAC was one of the first examples of a massive digital computer.

- Another reason why digital became the mode of computing is because of an enormously important piece of technology that was invented at Bell Labs in the 1940s: the transistor. Before that, electronic computers—whether digital or analog—used vacuum tubes to do the counting.

- Unlike vacuum tubes—which were bulky, used a lot of energy, were fragile, and were easy to overheat—the transistor was cheap, sturdy, used little power, worked instantly, and was tiny. Transistors have become even smaller with time, and because they're so much smaller, we can make a whole lot more of them.

- We can now put about 3 billion transistors on a single computer chip, and because so many are made at a time, the cost of making a transistor has decreased substantially. Transistors are often integrated with many other electronic components—such as resistors, capacitors, and diodes—to produce complete electronic circuits.

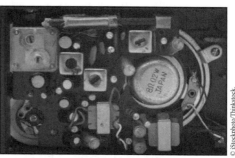

Today, the cost of making a transistor is comparable to the cost of printing a single letter in a newspaper.

© iStockphoto/Thinkstock.

- In 1965, Gordon Moore, who was a cofounder of the company Intel, famously outlined the promise of the continued miniaturization and lower cost of the transistor: He predicted that the number of transistors on a chip would double every 24 months. Amazingly, for 45 years, this has been the guiding principle of the high-tech industry.

Computing in Our World

- Computing has revolutionized movie making, bringing the convergence of real and imaginary worlds on film. It has allowed for greater accuracy in weather prediction, enabled highly complex automation, and brought about a new era of medical diagnostics as well as drug discovery and design.

- Because of the computing power we have, we can now simulate materials all the way down to the scale of a single electron, allowing us to invent and optimize new materials computationally before trying to make them in the laboratory.

- Now that we've reached a new age of being able to actually make and control materials at the scale of a single atom, this type of computer simulation is of paramount importance to the discovery, screening, and rapid prototyping of such new materials.

- Today, we can do what is known as true multi-scale modeling, where the behavior of the world can be simulated all the way from the scale of the building down to the scale of the atom and electron. At each length and timescale for the problem at hand, the computer simulates the fundamental laws of physics or chemistry to predict how the material will behave.

- The term **modeling** refers to the development of a mathematical representation of a physical situation. On the other hand, **simulation** refers to the procedure of solving the equations that result from model development.

- We're getting pretty close to reaching a size below which we can no longer make a transistor. As much as you can scale the size of a semiconductor material down, you cannot scale the size of an atom down.

- Not too long from now, we will reach a point where physical limits of atomic structures or power densities will be reached. Over the past several decades, many have incorrectly predicted a near end to Moore's law, but there is certainly a limit.

- The amount of heat these densely packed chips generate is another challenge. The more transistors that are packed on a chip, the more electrons there are flowing through the same amount of area—which creates so much heat that thermal management is becoming a key limiting factor.

- On the other hand, there are ways to cram more and more transistors into a single chip. One technique is to use 3-dimensionality in chip design as opposed to having everything laid out in 2 dimensions. This allows the wiring between transistors on the chip to be closer together, which shortens the distance that information needs to travel within the chip—leading to greater efficiencies and more pathways for travel.

- However, 3-D technologies are still very much in the research stage, and big challenges have to be overcome—such as how to efficiently cool the chip. Chips get extremely hot, and in 3-D, it's a bigger challenge to get the heat out than it is in 2-D.

- Another idea that could extend the life of Moore's law is to improve the way the information in the chip flows and how logic is carried out. The transistor is only a building block, but the chip is a highly complex set of these transistors, arranged with other electronics.

- The current standard technology is known as CMOS (complementary metal-oxide semiconductor), which represents a particular way of constructing the logic functions. However, there may be more efficient ways to build and integrate electronic components in a chip, and there will certainly be advances in this area.

- After 50 years, it's time for the transistor—even with 3-dimensionality—to be outdone and outperformed by a new technology in the same way the transistor itself replaced vacuum tubes. That new technology has yet to be determined, but there are a number of approaches scientists are exploring and working on.

Future Computing Technologies

- One possible future technology is called **optical computing**. In this concept, information travels and is also processed as light, or photons, as opposed to electrons. The advantage is that photons travel faster than electrons, and a whole lot more of them can travel in a wire of the same size. Information is already routinely piped through optical fibers.

- The first real applications of optics in computing could occur in a hybrid sense, where electrons do the computing but are then converted into light to be further computed. However, if we wanted a fully optical computer, then we'd need to be able to build logic operations out of light—which would need not just a highway for information (the wire), but also a switch (a transistor).

- Scientists have already been able to design optical transistors, ones that use one laser beam to control the intensity of another. There are many hurdles that still need to be overcome, but the promise of computers that run on light is very real and very exciting.

- Another kind of futuristic computing is known as **quantum computing**. This approach would not only allow us to reach miniaturizations far beyond the predictions of Moore's law, but it would also allow us to solve existing problems with significantly fewer operations.

- Quantum computing has the potential to tackle some problems— particularly in areas like encryption—that computers using traditional approaches are unable to even formulate.

- In a quantum computer, the fundamental unit of information— called a quantum bit, or qubit—is not binary as it is with the computers we know today. Instead, it is quaternary in nature, a property that arises as a direct consequence of its adherence to the laws of quantum mechanics, which differ radically from the laws of classical physics.

- A qubit can exist not only in a state corresponding to the logical state 0 or 1 as in a classical bit, but also in states corresponding to a blend or superposition of these classical states. In other words, a qubit can exist as a 0, a 1, or simultaneously as both 0 and 1.

- The potential power of quantum computing comes from the possibility of performing a mathematical operation on both states simultaneously; however, there are some complications that cause this area to be developed today by scientists.

- In spintronics, the fundamental information carrier that's processed and sent around the insides of a computer chip could be the spin of an electron as opposed to the electron itself. If we could create transistors and logic circuits using spin instead of electrons, the information could be transferred and processed much more quickly and with less power.

- A DNA computer uses pieces of short, single-stranded DNA that send signals—just like electrons in a traditional chip—by interacting with one another and creating new strands. Certain DNA strands are used to input the starting values of a computation in digital format, and others are used as reporter molecules that change colors to signify the answer.

- Logic gates made with DNA that can perform "and," "or," and "not" functions have already been demonstrated. The advantage in DNA computing will likely never be in speed; rather, they would be a new kind of computer that can interact directly with components within living cells.

- With the further miniaturization of electronics and development of lower-power computing, there could be hundreds of billions of embedded chips and sensing devices embedded in the physical world in products or materials and spread pervasively throughout our environment. This is called **ubiquitous computing**, and many believe that it will be the next era of computing.

Important Terms

modeling: Refers to the development of a mathematical representation of a physical situation.

optical computing: In this concept, information travels and is also processed as light, or photons, as opposed to electrons.

quantum computing: A kind of futuristic computing that would allow us to solve existing problems with significantly fewer operations. In this approach, the fundamental unit of information—called a quantum bit, or qubit—is not binary as it is with computers. Instead, it is quaternary in nature, a property that arises as a direct consequence of its adherence to the laws of quantum mechanics, which differ radically from the laws of classical physics.

simulation: Refers to the procedure of solving the equations that result from model development.

ubiquitous computing: A kind of futuristic computing in which computing devices could be so small that they would be deeply embedded in the physical world in products or materials—or even human skin—and spread pervasively throughout our environment like smart grains of sand or dust.

Suggested Reading

Bandyopadhyay and Cahay, *Introduction to Spintronics*.

Brock, *Understanding Moore's Law*.

Rieffel and Polak, *Quantum Computing*.

Scientific American, *Understanding Supercomputing*.

Questions to Consider

1. What is Moore's law, and when and why will it end?

2. What comes next?

Artificial Intelligence—Thinking Machines
Lecture 5

T he electronic revolution enabled the development of high-performance computing, and the high-level computations now possible suggest the possibility of having artificial intelligence. While this was and is a long-sought promise, we don't see much artificial intelligence in our lives today because there's so much we still have to learn about how and why we humans are intelligent. The future of artificial intelligence will be intricately connected with the future of our understanding of human intelligence, and—perhaps one day—vice versa.

Artificial Intelligence

- **Artificial intelligence (AI)** is the science and engineering of making intelligent machines. The basic idea behind artificial intelligence is to be able to replicate the capabilities of our human mind. This means that the definition of AI goes far beyond the ability to perform quick calculations; it requires independent thinking based on a set of environmental inputs.

- The basic idea that sparked the quest for artificial intelligence is that the brain, like any other organ, can be considered as a collection of small parts. The idea was that even thoughts could potentially be made artificially.

- Alan Turing, who most consider to be the father of AI, proposed that any properly designed machines able to sort binary bits—that is, able to shuffle around a bunch of 1s and 0s—could simulate any conceivable act of mathematical deduction. Remarkably, Turing developed this theory before computers were really invented.

- The Turing machine concept was enormously powerful in the 1930s and sparked a great deal of interest in computers, computing, and artificial intelligence. However, today—nearly 80 years later—there still is not a working AI machine even close to being similar to our brain. Part of the problem is that not everything our brain does can be considered as an act of mathematical deduction.

- The first AI programs started to appear in the 1960s, when we had computers that were fast enough. By today's standards, these computers were not so fast—about a whopping 10 million times slower.

- At the time, these AI programs were considered to be simply astonishing in their capabilities. They could solve math equations, prove logical theorems, and, in some cases, even speak a language.

- For example, a program named Eliza was able to act like a therapist, "listening" to statements typed in by the "patient" and responding with seemingly intelligent follow-up questions or statements. The idea that a computer could answer questions we could ask it was beyond anything imaginable.

- Considering the example of Eliza, we immediately see the limitations of this early approach to AI: All the program does is use simple pattern-matching techniques and take canned responses from a list. This is not true intelligence; it's more like the difference between memorization and problem solving.

- Today, this is known as a chatterbox. As long as the questions to the computer are simple and predictable, these programs can find a match, rephrase something from your words into one of its stored sentences, determine it to be in line with grammar rules, and give you a reply.

- With such a simple approach, any deviation in our questions into the realm of the unpredictable was sufficient to pose problems for Eliza. Even if this misleading approach had worked to some extent, there were other issues that would have limited it quite severely.

Challenges for AI

- The lack of computational power in the early days of computing limited the programmed-response approach to AI. However, this issue was soon overcome by the explosive growth in computing power.

- Much more limiting is the massive amount of possible combinations of factors necessary for an answer to a question. The more articulate the question, the larger the range of possibilities. This is what still limits even today's massive computational power from being sufficient.

- Humans are able to use fast, intuitive judgment rather than the step-by-step deduction process of computers. Unfortunately, while ways to parallelize problem-solving capabilities in computers exist, the process is still not adequate to replicate even a fraction of what humans can do.

- Automated planning is arguably one of the most important aspects of AI. Planning is directly connected to the ability to make a decision—for a human, it involves setting goals and taking into account constant feedback about predictions that the brain receives with fast reaction times. Planning is crucial in our daily lives—for even simple goals.

- Currently, when we give a problem to a computer, it simply takes however long it needs to solve the problem by running a particular software program. Planning never really enters into the process. Real planning, as obvious as it is for us, is incredibly complex.

- Another major challenge for the future of AI is learning. This is a key prerequisite of AI. It takes years to train a brain to do what it does, and the process of learning is highly complex and not necessarily very well defined. The same applies to AI. We need to figure out how to write programs that can learn.

- AI must also have a way of classifying information so that it is truly learned. If it doesn't store enough or classify the information correctly, it may not know enough to recognize the same thing later, but if it stores this new event in too much detail, it may never find anything else like it again—also rendering the learning useless.

- Other challenges in AI are natural language processing and the understanding of nonverbal communication. Communication goes well beyond spoken words; it also involves our body. This complex scheme of communication is something an AI machine will need to be able to understand and reproduce.

- For any AI system to meet these challenges, it's going to need enormous amounts of information about the world—such as the Internet. However, having a large stack of information at their disposal doesn't make computers more intelligent.

- Therefore, for AI to work, it not only needs to be able to access vast amounts of stored information, but it needs an aggressive and lightning-fast way to assess the quality and relevance of this information—and then it needs to be able to make a decision.

Watson: Modern-Day Eliza

- In early 2011, a computer built by IBM named Watson made a groundbreaking performance—it appeared on the television show *Jeopardy* and managed to beat 2 of the greatest human players of the game.

- Watson has a very complex set of algorithms that provide a complex answer to an equally complex question; it is able to understand a language, but it is still not able to really think.

- In the future, AI will become more than just signal processing. For AI to work, it needs a specific task that requires the machine to follow the author's argument (reason); it needs to know what is being talked about (knowledge); and then it needs to faithfully reproduce the author's intention (social intelligence).

- Today, even the cutting-edge demonstrations of AI like Watson are programmed for very specific tasks, but in the future, we'll need to program computers with the general ability to solve many different problems as opposed to doing a single one very well.

Task-Specific AI
- Exciting examples of AI come from places that might not be obvious at first, such as on the road. Self-driving cars have been developed for the past 20 years and are now smart enough to make decisions based on highly complex input from the environment. Tests ranging from dense city traffic to highways to cross-country terrain have demonstrated remarkable success.

- It may take a while for us to trust these cars to drive us around, but the technology and, most importantly, the AI is in place to do it. We already have cars that can parallel park themselves; in the future, cars will very likely be driving themselves.

- Even when the task is seemingly trivial, like vacuuming the floor, the AI inside an appliance has to be able to understand its surrounding unknown environment through a host of sensors and then make decisions about where to move next.

- A much more challenging but still highly specific application of AI is in what is known as predictive **data mining**, which is essentially what our brain does when looking for a solution to a problem—only it can do it in massively parallel mode. Data mining involves the exploration of vast amounts of data and looking for consistent patterns.

- The immediate application for AI is with robots, which are machines waiting for a brain. On the other hand, AI is the brain that is waiting for a body. The 2 are advancing at an astronomical pace, and it is the merging of the 2 that excites many people.

- Researchers have realized that AI must be expanded to encompass many more scientific disciplines in order to fully integrate all of the sensory inputs and outputs directly with the "thinking" that goes on.

The Future of AI

- In the near future, we will see many more task-specific AI applications. In some cases, we will interact with these programs, like when we search the Internet. In fact, more sophisticated searching algorithms can be developed than exist today.

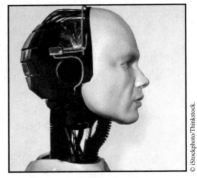

- Speech recognition—something long promised by AI—is now here, and we will see many more voice-controlled machines, from the stove to the car to our computers themselves. In this near-term future, applications that use AI will continue to exploit only very narrow and specific applications.

The idea that the brain, like any other organ, can be considered as a collection of small parts sparked the quest for artificial intelligence.

- It's going to take some time to reach the point at which AI has full artificial consciousness. Many wonder whether we can ever truly build a machine that can achieve artificial consciousness.

- Out of all of the ingredients we'll need to reach artificial consciousness, probably the hardest part will still be artificially creating social intelligence that is highly sensitive to subjective experiences. Will a computer ever be able to taste wine, feel a headache, or appreciate the beauty of a gorgeous sunset?

- In the future, we will build robots that realize what's happening when a person makes eye contact with them. We'll build robots that can respond to social cues in a variety of settings. They will be able to help children with disabilities, fight side by side with our soldiers in battle, and become effective teachers.

- What makes the human brain special—and what makes humans so diverse—is the fact that each one of us has a different experience and uses it to make decisions accordingly. This level of subjectivity makes it rather difficult to translate experiences immediately into mathematical algorithms, which are objective by definition.

- As AI machines acquire a more personalized way of learning, we will start to see the first bits of subjective experience in AI. This will be a great opportunity for AI because the introduction of diversity in AI will most likely also lead to self-healing and self-evolution. In other words, AI will improve itself based on its needs—just like our brain.

Important Terms

artificial intelligence (AI): The science and engineering of making intelligent machines. The basic idea behind this is to be able to replicate the capabilities of the human mind.

data mining: Essentially, this is what our brain does when looking for a solution to a problem, but artificial intelligence can do it in massively parallel mode. This process involves the exploration of vast amounts of data and looking for consistent patterns.

Suggested Reading

Russell and Norvig, *Artificial Intelligence.*

Scientific American, Understanding Artificial Intelligence.

1. How do we think—in serial or in parallel—and what does that even mean?

2. So far, artificial intelligence has been limited to fairly simple data retrieval and analysis. How is the complexity of machine thought being expanded now and into the future?

Robotics—Living with Machines
Lecture 6

Computing and artificial intelligence are both groundbreaking fields, but they are of course confined to the realm of the computer. Combining the advances in those fields with a mechanical device, extending the capabilities of computing and artificial intelligence to the physical world, results in the field of robotics. Given the advances in computing and the achievements in materials and in understanding the way the brain operates, we should not be surprised if the days of *The Terminator* are approaching in the not-too-distant future.

Robots versus Living Organisms

- The most basic definition of a **robot** is simply an electromechanical machine that is guided by a computer or artificial intelligence to perform a variety of tasks, from the most specific to the most general. A robot is programmed to perform a task either repetitively or by its own algorithms.

- Examples of robots we see today range from humanoid robots, to manufacturing robots for assembly lines, to unmanned aerial vehicles (drones) used in surveillance.

- Conversely, synthetic life is artificial life created from nonliving substances. It belongs to the discipline of synthetic biology, and this is usually distinguished from mechanical life that belongs to the discipline of robotics.

- Both robots and living organisms aim to perform the same tasks, at least to some extent, and to have the same functionality. However, while they might have a common goal, the difference resides mostly in the way such functionality is achieved.

- One of the key components to robotic life is power. A living organism uses food as its main source for power. A robot, in a way, is a lot simpler because the "brain" and "muscles" of a robot run directly on electric current.

- Energy for robots is stored in conventional batteries. The problem with batteries is their weight. While food is used up, the weight of a battery is there to stay at all times. Also, batteries do not have the same energy density as food, and they require long recharging times.

- The future of power generation will certainly overcome these limitations. Future robots will be able to run on more than just flowing electrons. For example, they may be able to process organic material such as biomass in a way that is not so different than our own digestive system to produce either fuel or electric power directly.

- An actuator is essentially what allows any mechanical motion in a robot. Current robots use either electric motors or pneumatics as actuators.

© Stockbyte/Thinkstock.

Manufacturing robots are used in assembly lines to make the process automatic and to eliminate the human element.

- Although pneumatics require a high-pressure system with electric pumps, they can sustain high loads and large ranges of operation. Electric motors are more compact and lighter, but they require large energy-storage systems to operate.

- One thing that will be different in the future is that just as we have many different types of muscles in our bodies, the future of robots will bring us completely new and radical technologies for actuators.

- Obviously, having the ability to move isn't very useful for a robot unless it also has sensors, just like it wouldn't be useful for humans to have motion without our senses. Robots may need as many senses as humans have; in particular, eyesight, touch, and smell will be of crucial importance for robots of the future.

- While cameras are widespread and inexpensive, touch sensors are less common and fairly coarse in their action. Pressure, texture, and heat sensors that are more localized and sensitive will allow robots to much more deeply understand the feel of an object.

- In the near future, a robot will be able to smell with the use of an electronic nose. This will allow the robot to follow chemical traces, which is very important in applications such as search and recovery.

Robots and Communication
- We are inclined to think of robots as expressionless machines, but to really perform like we do, they will need to communicate like we do. Research shows that nonverbal communication among humans accounts for 93% of our communication.

- For a robot to interact at the same level with humans, they would need to be able to use and understand body language, which accounts for much of our nonverbal communication. Robots would need to recognize, interpret, and appropriately reproduce gestures, facial expressions, and emotions.

- Hollywood has helped define humanlike behavior. In the movie *Wall-E*, for example, most of the interactions between robots are carried out nonverbally through controlled gestures. We humans have no problems identifying the "feelings" and "emotions" in such robotic expressions.

- Many robotics labs are working tirelessly on the challenge of mimicking human expressions. This is not just today's dream for robotics; the goal has been the same since the beginning of robotics—namely, the vision of perfecting the way we can accurately mimic nature.

Attempts at Mimicking Humans

- In 1739, the Digesting Duck was a prototype created that aimed to replicate the processes that enable digestion in animals. This prototype appeared to have the ability to eat and digest kernels of grain.

- In 1937, Elektro, a fully anthropomorphic robot, was built. It was a 7-foot-tall, 265-pound, human-looking robot that could walk by voice command, speak about 700 words, smoke cigarettes, blow up balloons, tell the difference between red and green light, and move its head and arms.

- While robots that can do very specific tasks exist, actions like cooking a full meal followed by cleaning the table and loading the dishwasher fall in the world of *The Jetsons*. Those that can do those types of activities, and many more, do not exist yet.

- ASIMO, which stands for Advanced Step in Innovative Mobility, is a fully anthropomorphic robot that can walk, run, play soccer, shake hands, and perform a variety of other quite remarkable tasks. The current price of around a million dollars will most certainly fall dramatically as less expensive designs are invented. ASIMO is currently one of the most technologically advanced machines ever built.

- In addition to cost, there is another very important limiting factor that severely restricts the range of action of robots such as ASIMO: power. With today's battery technology, ASIMO can operate for 45 minutes but takes 3 hours of charging time. For a fully functional android, that is far too limiting.

- The development of new power sources is paramount for making new, efficient, lightweight robots—that is, assuming that we really need such multifunctional robots.

- Even though we have had for 70 years and still have a dream of humanoid robots "living" alongside humans, in some ways, it may be better to consider whether that should really be our ultimate goal. We can use robotics to help humans replicate and enhance parts of us as opposed to interacting with us as a whole.

Bionic Humans and Cyborgs
- The quest for a bionic human develops alongside the goals of robotics. Some of the artificial or bionic components that would replace parts of our body are still quite a ways in the future, such as retinal implants to re-enable vision in blind people. However, others are quite real, such as limb prosthetics. Today, there are even examples of prosthetic limbs that outperform real legs.

- The word **cyborg** is used to define a person with mechanical or electronic parts implanted in his or her body to supplement or improve upon human deficiencies. In many cases, these kinds of implants are lifesavers—or at least life changers. Therefore, the bionic human already exists, although not exactly with the kind of superpowers we thought it would have.

- As with many other advances in science and technology, the battlefield has proven to be one of the key places that drives development and testing of many robotic technologies. Unmanned aerial vehicles (UAVs) are widely used for surveillance and, in some cases, attack.

- Unmanned ground vehicles used in battle are highly complex, able to go into much harsher environments than human soldiers. Prototype bodysuits able to improve human strength or provide ultrasensitive environmental data have already been developed and tested.

- Today, robots are being used for surgery, even though a human being is still driving the robotic arms. Regardless, such capabilities can enable a new range of possibilities, such as having a remote surgery performed with an actual surgeon driving the robots from miles away or even across a continent.

- In the future, such surgeries may even be fully automated with an AI robot, but for now, just extending the range of a surgeon to be remote opens enormous possibilities.

- Another way robots are used in surgery is to perform microsurgery—for very small areas, where hands cannot reach. In fact, in small areas is where a lot of next-generation robotics research is directed.

Robots of the Future
- We often think of robots as machines made of large mechanical parts. However, one of the most important contributions from robotics in the future may come from microrobots and nanorobots. These tiny robots would be able to access places that cannot be reached with hands or with conventional tools and would be used not only for surgery, but also for medical diagnostics.

- In fact, future robots could exist that are created starting from the level of the atom by carefully assembling atoms and molecules to form new smart machines.

- Nanorobots are largely in the research-and-development phase, but some primitive molecular machines have been built and tested. A useful application of nanorobotics might be in medical technology, where they could be used to identify and destroy cancer cells.

Another potential application is the detection and measurement of toxic chemicals in the environment.

- Because nanorobots would be microscopic in size, it is likely that very large numbers of them would work together to perform specific tasks. These nanorobot swarms haven't made it into real demonstrations yet, but they are certainly found in many sci-fi stories.

- There are many concerns around nanorobots—for example, with ones that could self-replicate. Fortunately, most scientists working in this area agree that the process of self-replication, if it were ever to be developed, could be made inherently safe.

- The simplest approach is to have robots be **avatars**, or mechanical bodies for humans to exploit, with their "life" coming from humans. These are virtual cyborgs in the way that all of the body is replaced, but the controlling mind is not.

- Today, avatars are still sci-fi, but not completely; in gaming, such augmented reality already exists. The inexpensive power of computing is already being combined with robotics to allow for augmented reality. We'll be seeing a whole lot more of this type of avatar robotics in the near future.

- AI is a very articulate and complex field. Because robotics is the body of the AI brain, properly designed AI will be needed not only to fully take advantage of all the possibilities in robotics, but also to prove that robots can perhaps evolve themselves, improving their own design. For this to happen, robots will need to acquire self-consciousness and self-awareness.

Important Terms

avatar: A mechanical body for humans to exploit, with its "life" coming from humans. These are virtual cyborgs in the way that all of the body is replaced, but the controlling mind is not.

cyborg: A person with mechanical or electronic parts implanted in his or her body to supplement or improve upon human deficiencies.

robot: An electromechanical machine that is guided by a computer or artificial intelligence to perform a variety of tasks, from the most specific to the most general. A robot is programmed to perform a task either repetitively or by its own algorithms.

Suggested Reading

Freedman, *Robots through History*.

Singer, *Wired for War*.

Strom, *From Bugbots to Humanoids*.

Questions to Consider

1. What makes a robot a robot?

2. What is the most limiting factor in the future of both highly specialized robots as well as fully functional humanoid robots?

Microscopes—The Power of Seeing It All

Lecture 7

In this lecture, we'll be learning about using technology to expand our senses and, in particular, how to use microscopes to expand our ability to see into the world of the small. The idea of the microscope is to allow us to see beyond our eyes—or, more generally, beyond our senses. In the past, the need to look at ever-smaller objects focused the development of microscopes toward improved resolution. The needs of today to understand and solve global challenges will drive the development of our next generation of microscopes.

Vision and Visual Acuity

- Perfect vision, also described as 20/20 vision, means that at a distance of 20 feet you can distinguish between 2 objects. In other words, they appear as 2 objects and not as one. If they were to appear as a single object, we would say that you had lost the resolution.

- Different animals have very different resolutions. A rat, for example, can't see nearly as well as a person, while a hawk can see with almost 10 times the resolution of a human.

- **Visual acuity** is what sets the limit of what we can see and what we cannot see. We need visual acuity much greater than a hawk in order to answer some of the most important science questions of our time.

- If we can see tiny things, then we can study them, and if we can study them, we can understand and build useful technologies around them. The way to this lies in our devices; namely, we need to be able to make devices that increase our visual acuity. Historically, this is what has happened.

Understanding Microscopes

- A camera is not a microscope. The difference is in the lenses and the ways in which they are used to change the **optics**, which refers to the path of the light itself. Basically, a microscope is like a camera but with a lot more ways to modify the image.

- We've been trying to enhance light with lenses for more than 500 years—all the way back to the time of Galileo who, along with a number of others, was able to build some of the very first microscopes by using lenses to enhance the light by a factor of 10 times. It took another 200 years before the technology to record images was invented.

- Around the same time as the earliest microscopes, a very important advance occurred: The achromatic lens was developed. On large scales, such a lens wouldn't make a difference, although it can be noticeable.

- As you get down to small sizes, the problem arises from the fact that different colors of light are deflected by a lens in different directions. Therefore, there's a dependence of where an object will be focused, on the color within the object.

- On the scales of objects that our own eyes see, this dependence is small enough that we don't need to correct for it; in fact, our eyes don't do any correction for this.

- This color-dependent focusing at smaller scales was known to be a problem long ago and was corrected by modifying the shape of the lens itself, resulting in the achromatic lens.

- All light is a wave with a given wavelength, and light can exist at any wavelength, but it's only a very narrow set of wavelengths in which we are able to see light. This is called the visible part of the spectrum; the wavelengths in this part of the spectrum range in size from 400–700 nm.

- The diffraction limit is the way in which we see an object and how these waves combine together and interfere with that object. Diffraction limit is related to the size of the object we want to try to look at.

Optical Light and Electrons

- Electrons also have wavelengths, and they can also be used as the light source to try to see things. The nice thing about using electrons is that they can cover a pretty broad range of size.

- If we want to see at those tiny scales, we can't just use the corresponding wavelength of light because it's difficult to generate a bright source of light at those wavelengths.

- Conceptually, the processes of using optical light and electrons are very similar. Lenses are still used, but instead of using light from a lightbulb to illuminate an image electrons are used as the light source.

- Examples of technologies that use electrons as the light source are the megapowerful transition and scanning electron microscopes. The act of seeing objects with these kinds of microscopes, ones that use electrons as the light source, is known as **electron microscopy**.

- The development of electron microscopy is relatively recent, and it has played an enormous role in many of the scientific and technological accomplishments in materials science, electronics, and biology for the past 60 years.

- With electron microscopy, we can see objects that we could not normally see with an optical microscope based on visible light; we can see all the way down to the atomic level—atoms on a surface or even nanoscale objects. We can also use electron microscopy to look at larger objects, things that we could potentially also see with optical microscopy.

- Using electrons as the light source can give greater detail and enhanced resolution. Basically, electron microscopy took the science of microscopes to a whole new level, revealing new micromaterials and nanomaterials that would not otherwise have been possible to characterize and study before.

Scientists use microscopes to expand their ability to see into the world of the small.

- With electron microscopy, we still use lenses when the source of light is electrons, but the lens needs to be made differently. As with optical microscopes, the point is to use a lens to bend the light, but now this bending is accomplished using magnets instead of a piece of glass.

- Through the development of new magnetic materials, lenses have been crafted that are able to carefully bend the light with great accuracy. In this case, microscopes were used to investigate new materials that were then used to build the next generation of microscopes.

- In a general sense, electron microscopes are similar to optical microscopes; therefore, they may suffer from some of the same issues. Because of some of these issues, it's crucial for an electron microscope to have a range of wavelengths as close as possible to zero (monochromaticity). In other words, in electron microscopes, we want the light to be of only one color.

The Advancement of Microscopes

- Think of microscopes as fingers spanning over a Braille book; scanning probe microscopes basically work in the same way. By taking a very sharp tip and scanning it across the surface of a material, we can probe its topography, or surface structure, as well as other properties.

- How far we can see—or perhaps "feel"—with such scanning probe microscopes depends on the size of the "fingers" that we use. Actually, using tools developed with electron microscopes, we can make really sharp fingers. In fact, they can be so sharp that the tip is made only of a handful of atoms.

- With scanning probe microscopes, the resolution depends on the size of the tip. It seems, in principle, easier to use this finger approach rather than using electron microscopes, but in science and technology, we use both because they are complementary to one another, each having its own strengths and weaknesses.

- In these scanning probe techniques (using touch), we only see the surface of the material; electron microscopy can instead probe all of the material at once. Scanning probes are great for materials in which we are particularly interested in surface properties. These tactile microscopes are also great when we want to manipulate atoms at the surface.

- Electron microscopes are still essential because they provide a picture of the whole material, not just its surface, and they're also much faster at taking their pictures. With electron microscopes, we can see what's inside a nanoscale object and how atoms are arranged as we go deeper into a material.

- Today, top laboratories rely on both techniques rather than on just one of them. In fact, they are so complementary that scientists are trying to develop hybrid microscopes that actually can combine these 2 techniques.

- Combining different kinds of microscopy together into a single microscope is become more and more common as scientists find new ways to merge technologies.

- By scaling down the size of the lenses to the same size of the objects we want to see in the nanoworld, we can again push the resolution beyond the diffraction limit simply because we magnify the size of the smaller object through nanolenses so that the magnified image on the lens is above the diffraction limit and, therefore, can be observed with a regular optical microscope.

- If we look at what other possible light we can use, the next natural light source would be X-rays. The size and technological complexity of current X-ray microscopes prevent them from being widespread.

- Generating X-rays isn't nearly as easy as generating electrons. For X-rays, you need a powerful particle accelerator called a synchrotron, which is the size of a large building, and then you need to create X-ray bending lenses, which are pretty complex as well.

Seeing Electrons as Particles

- The rules of quantum mechanics are pretty clear: We cannot accurately measure both the position and the velocity (momentum) of a particle the size of an electron or below. We won't be able to see electrons as particles, no matter how we design our microscopes.

- Scientists figured out that we might be able to use a completely different approach to see subatomic matter. Researchers have built particle accelerators that are so large that they have the dimensions of a small city.

- These experiments probe the existence of subatomic particles and ultimately enable a better comprehension of the building block of atoms. However, while improvements will continue in these so-called atom smashers, cost and feasibility of implementing such large-scale projects are a strong motivation to scale down to a more reasonable and accessible scale.

Microscopes of the Future

- Electron microscopes are great tools to probe inorganic materials, or nonliving materials, but because of the large energy the electrons carry, they can have a negative impact on the specimen itself—such as damage and degradation.

- Using electron microscopes in biology is so far not very common because of the potential harm, and this is an extremely hot research topic in today's development of better microscopes. There's great excitement and expectation of groundbreaking technological advances that would come with the ability to someday probe delicate biological materials with atomic resolution.

- Scientists often use their imaginations to build a 3-D model from 2-D microscopy images. The field of tomography is currently exploring ways to probe a material and to image it in 3 dimensions with the aid of 3-D imaging technology.

- Most electron microscopy is done in a vacuum because if it were done in normal air, the image would be distorted, limiting visual acuity. However, the ability to see chemical reactions as they occur and to see how nanomaterials grow, evolve, and interact with the outside world would be extremely powerful.

- Just as miniaturization of electronics led to the development of information technology, enabling a new way of living, miniaturization of microscopy could enable the development of a whole new set of opportunities and possibilities in biology and medicine.

Important Terms

electron microscopy: The act of seeing objects with microscopes that use electrons as the light source.

optics: The study of light and how light travels through and between materials.

visual acuity: This is what sets the limit of what we can see and what we cannot see.

Croft, *Under the Microscope*.

Murphy, *Fundamentals of Light Microscopy and Electronic Imaging*.

Questions to Consider

1. Is light the only thing we use to "see" things, and what sets the limit of how small we can see?

2. Why don't we have X-ray vision?

Nanotechnology—The New Science of Small
Lecture 8

A nanometer is extremely small. To be specific, a typical sheet of paper is 100,000 nanometers thick. The ability to observe and construct things this small is at the heart of nanotechnology. The science and technology of tomorrow will have a lot to do with nanotechnology, which could revolutionize the way we live in countless ways. In this first lecture of 2 nanotechnology lectures, we'll learn what nanotechnology is, how we define it, and what happens to materials at scales of this size.

The History of Nanotechnology

- About 50 years ago, the physicist Richard Feynman gave a famous speech in which the idea of nanotechnology was first envisioned. In it, he wondered what would happen if we could arrange atoms the way we want them. He was way ahead of his time.

- It took 30 years for microscopes to be developed, making it possible for his groundbreaking vision to be realized and letting scientists for the first time both see and manipulate matter at the atomic scale.

- In 1999, President Clinton launched the National Nanotechnology Initiative—the first large-scale U.S. government investment in nanoscale science, engineering, and technology—a program whose budget has more than tripled today and continues to grow.

- Despite this rapidly growing field filled with enormous promise, even the basic definition of nanotechnology itself is still heavily debated. A definition that has gained quite a bit of consensus is that **nanotechnology** is the purposeful engineering of matter at scales of less than 100 nanometers to achieve size-dependent properties and functions.

- The central points of nanotechnology are represented in this statement: First, nanotechnology should be purposeful, not by accident; second, the size scale is less than 100 nanometers; and third, it involves properties that are size dependent.

- Nanotechnology holds the key to meeting global energy needs with clean solutions, providing abundant clean water globally, increasing the health and longevity of human life, maximizing the productivity of agriculture, making powerful information technology available everywhere, and even enabling the development of space.

- The market for nanotechnology-based products is predicted by many to be trillions of dollars within another decade, and nearly every sector of the economy will be impacted.

- However, when one surveys the products based on nanotechnology that are available today, we do not come away with such an impressive picture. The promise of nanotechnology is real, but there is also just a lot of hype to get attention and funding.

- A **nanometer** is, by definition, a billionth of a meter. A piece of paper is 100,000 times thicker than that. If a meter were the size of the planet Earth, then a nanometer would be the size of a marble.

- Nanoparticles have been exploited by humans for millennia. The Egyptians used nanoparticle dyes to make glass beads, and nanoparticles have also been used to color clothes for many decades.

- Nanotechnology means taking advantage of known nanoscale properties to purposefully engineer new materials. Today, the age of nanotechnology is based, not so much on a particular element or material, but rather on our new abilities to design materials at the atomic scale.

Tuning the Properties of Materials and Devices

- A size of less than 100 nm is an important size range because of quantum effects; in nanoscale materials, the quantum mechanical properties of matter can dominate over bulk properties—big chunks of the material as opposed to nanoscale ones.

- The color, or more broadly speaking, the optical properties of a material, involve the wavelength of light that the material absorbs and emits. For many materials, as they enter into the nanoscale size regime, the wavelength of light that the object emits can change.

- Simply by changing the size of a material to the nanoscale, we can control the color of the material, completely opening up to variation this once-rigid attribute. This effect is due to something known as quantum confinement: If you take something in the macro world and break off a smaller piece from that, the color certainly doesn't change, but at the nanoscale, new properties emerge—ones that can be controlled—simply by changing the size.

- In addition to quantum effects, a second key reason that the nanoscale size regime is special is because of the dramatic increase in the surface-to-volume ratio. When the size of a material gets smaller, the surface area of the material can increase even while the volume remains the same.

- This effect occurs at all length scales, but what makes it unique at the nanoscale is that the properties of the material become strongly dependent and, therefore, controllable on the surface of the material. Surface plays a hugely important role in technology.

- Because reactions occur at the interface of 2 substances, when a large percentage of the particles are located on the surface, we get maximum exposed surface area, which means maximum reactivity. Therefore, nanoscale materials can make amazing **catalysts**, which are chemicals that help reactions go faster or, simply, enable them to happen at all.

- Entirely new possibilities are opened in other applications as well, such as in filtering or in the development of completely new composite materials.

Advances in Nanotechnology

- Until very recently, we've thought that there were only 2 kinds of carbon—graphite and diamond—at least for materials where the atoms are ordered, as in a crystal. Fullerenes and nanotubes are a form of carbon we never knew existed until a few decades ago.

- The Nobel Prize was awarded for the discovery of fullerenes, which are also known as the third form of carbon. This new class of carbon is so important because it gives even more possible uses and technologies based on this very abundant, strong, inexpensive, and biocompatible material.

- The third reason that the size range of less than 100 nanometers is special is that this also happens to be the size regime of the fundamental building blocks of biology. The basic components of life are the ultimate forms of naturally occurring nanotechnology.

- DNA, which is the source code of life, is only 3 nanometers across. Viruses can be that small as well and are typically smaller than 50 nanometers. In addition, the molecules that form many of the other key ingredients to life, from enzymes to proteins, are in the nanometer size range.

- We are now capable of making and controlling materials that are at the same length scale as biology and medicine. For example, **quantum dots** are tiny chunks of matter. The size range for quantum dots—where the color can be tuned from purple, to blue, to yellow and red—are exactly in the size range of the individual letters of genetic code in DNA.

- This convergence of length scales means that nanostructures can be functionalized in such a way to interact with biological elements, leading to revolutionary possibilities for medical imaging, drug delivery, and repairing genes. Indeed, the emergent fields of nanobiology and nanomedicine are where some of the most exciting nanotechnology discoveries are originating.

- In nature, there are numerous examples of nanotechnology-based systems, already highly optimized through millions of years of evolutionary development. The tiny hairs within a frog's ear are part of an incredible, ultrasensitive, nanomechanical measurement system built by nature.

- Nature employs nanotechnology in various ways, but the most important one to us is the human body itself, which contains billions of nanoscale machines. It is both fascinating and humbling to observe that, despite all of the phenomenal technological advances in nanoscale synthesis and measurement, we are still unable to build nanotechnology-based devices that even come close to rivaling nature in most cases.

© Hemera/Thinkstock.

Benefits and Challenges of Nanotechnology

- In some cases, the benefit of nanotechnology will mean an incremental improvement in a well-

A small ant is about a million nanometers across, and so is a raindrop.

established process—for example, in the increase in the strength-to-weight ratio of a material that uses carbon nanotubes as opposed to the current carbon fibers.

- In other cases, the benefit will mean the ability to do something on a greater scale of magnitude or better than previously, depending on the application. For example, a sensor based on a nanomechanical resonator, like the ear hairs of frogs, may achieve the same levels of sensitivity but require 1/10 the power to operate.

- It's certainly true that major experimental advances over the past several decades have made the ability to create, manipulate, and measure atomic-scale phenomena nearly routine.

- Nevertheless, there are numerous scientific challenges that have to be addressed in order for this burgeoning field to live up to the high promise and potential that nanotechnologies might offer. All of these challenges require the confluence of disparate disciplines for the continuation of the current outstanding pace of progress.

- One example is in synthesis. The main challenge in all synthesis techniques is the amount to which key characteristics can be controlled during the synthesis process. At the nanoscale, this can be quite a challenge because the control has to happen at such small scales, especially when integrating one nanomaterial with another.

- Another example is in measuring the properties of nanomaterials. One of the greatest challenges of the nanoscale development community is that they are essentially still operating in a blind mode because present ways to look all the way down at these tiny scales are slow, very expensive, and may require low temperatures or vacuum conditions to operate effectively.

- The era of nanotechnology was first enabled by the development of superpowerful microscopes, but much further advances in our ability to see this world is going to be essential to progress in the field.

- In engineering, top-down manufacturing starts from a large piece of material and carves the desired smaller features. Bottom-up synthesis, on the other hand, starts from the smallest constituents, atoms or molecules, and assembles a final, large-scale structure. With nanotechnology, it will be critical to be able to blend top-down with bottom-up synthesis techniques.

- In addition, the fabrication and assembly of nanoscale components requires the expertise of an engineer combined with a kind of renaissance understanding of the chemistry, physics, and biology of the nanoscale. For this reason, nanoengineering will be a major profession of the future.

- The simulation of nanomaterials is another important challenge. With the amazing computational speed we now have, combined with 50 years of work on developing efficient computational tools, we are well positioned to solve the key equations that govern the behavior of materials. Today, we can predictively model the behavior of nanomaterials routinely using quantum mechanics.

Ethical Considerations

- Today, not enough information is known regarding both the toxicity and the potential exposure risks of nanotechnology-based devices. As with any scientific advance, we must balance the possible benefits of nanoscience research with possible harm.

- It is incumbent upon nanoscience research to proceed with caution. However, nanoscience research is self-regulating, peer reviewed, and a field where claims have to be backed by evidence.

- Because nanotechnology is highly likely to positively impact some of the most pressing problems facing our world, the potential rewards are so great that we must press ahead, even urgently, with nanoscience research, keeping mindful throughout of the need to balance benefit against risk.

Important Terms

catalyst: A chemical that helps reactions go faster or enables them to happen at all.

nanometer: One billionth of a meter.

nanotechnology: The purposeful engineering of matter at scales of less than 100 nanometers to achieve size-dependent properties and functions.

quantum dot: A tiny chunk of matter. The size range for quantum dots are in the size range of the individual letters of genetic code in DNA.

Suggested Reading

Drexler, *Engines of Creation*.

Foster, *Nanotechnology*.

Scientific American, Understanding Nanotechnology.

Questions to Consider

1. Is size enough for something to be nano? How do we define nanotechnology?

2. Name at least 2 things that are special about being so small.

Nanotechnology—Changing Everything
Lecture 9

There are numerous ways in which nanotechnology is set to change the world. In some cases, the benefit of nanotechnology will mean an incremental improvement in a well-established process. In other cases, the benefit will mean the ability to do something better than could have been done previously. In this lecture, we will discuss a mix of examples covering 4 basic areas that could provide revolutionary advantages over present-day technologies: new materials, energy, health, and the environment—representing only a small fraction of the scope of nanotechnology.

Nanotechnology and Revolutionary Materials

- Geckos are extraordinary animals. They're a kind of lizard who likes warm climates, eats mosquitoes for breakfast, and makes funny chirping sounds. Geckos can climb straight up a wall with nothing to anchor their feet and then keep walking across the ceiling because of their supersticky feet.

- On the feet of geckos is a very special kind of adhesive that leaves no residue, can be pointed in a given direction, is able to detach with almost no effort, is self-cleaning, and works underwater, in vacuum, and on just about every surface known.

- An adhesive that powerful could revolutionize the way we glue things together, from microsurgery in your body, to chip manufacturing, to robots that can walk on any surface, to astronauts on space walks. In addition, it's a technology that is completely based on nanotechnology.

- The adhesive is not due to chemistry or biochemistry. If you pressed a gecko toe onto a hard surface, it would not stick; the toe will only adhere when it's dragging or sliding in a direction parallel to the surface. With a gecko, it's all about nanoscale geometry.

- On the typical gecko's foot sit nearly a million tiny hairs, and the tip of each of these hairs splits into hundreds or thousands more. Each of those ends is shaped like a spatula—one so small that it has a diameter far less than the wavelength of visible light and a length of only a few hundred nanometers.

The nanoscale technology of gecko feet allow them to climb straight up a wall with nothing to anchor them.

- The fact that those tiny nanoscale spatulas are so small means they can lodge into nearly any surface to get a good grip. They're so small that, to them, the smoothest glass would appear bumpy and pitted.

- The way in which the gecko hairs do their sticking is not by the friction between their foot and the surface. Instead, the lizard takes advantage of the electrical forces between the tips of those hair molecules and the molecules of the surface. A gecko places its foot, palm first, and then uncurls each toe outward, thereby pushing each spatula hair flat against the surface.

- This gets the hair molecules so close to the surface molecules that they electrically bond for an instant with a force 600 times greater than friction. The force between the foot and the surface is due to unbalanced electrical charges around molecules attracting one another.

- To unstick, all that needs to happen is for the molecules in the spatula to get a little bit farther away from the surface—when they do, they very rapidly lose their sticking power. A tiny change in distance can lead to a huge drop in force.

- The gecko lifts the flattened spatula hair by restoring the angle that the hair shaft makes with the surface to 30 degrees; when that happens, the force drops and the hair pops off. This is how a gecko can have a foot that's always supersticky but can also be ready to run at any given moment.

- Progress to make a synthetic gecko tape has been immense in only a short time. People have wondered for millennia how gecko adhesion works, but it's only in the last few decades, with the use of much more powerful microscopes, that we've been able to unlock and understand the nanotechnology at hand.

- Now that we understand it, scientists are creating a wide range of materials that mimic the same principles; a wide range of materials could potentially be made to have these incredible adhesive properties.

Nanotechnology and Energy

- Researchers around the world are working on the development of alternative energy sources to fossil fuels—but each area of possible renewable resources faces major hurdles to becoming large-scale, cost-effective alternatives.

- The impact of nanotechnology on energy technologies is going to be enormous. For example, nanotechnology will contribute to the development of cheaper solar cells, new ultralow-water consumption plants for biofuels, new materials that could efficiently convert sunlight directly into hydrogen, higher energy density and faster charging batteries, and new materials that could safely and inexpensively store hydrogen as a fuel.

- Solar cells are devices that convert sunlight directly into electricity. The solar resource is by far the most plentiful renewable kind of energy we have, providing enough energy to power the world for a year in just 1 hour. Until now, solar cells have been dominated by a single material: silicon.

- When you take a piece of silicon and add some impurities to opposite ends, a charge imbalance across the material creates a field that generates an electric current when light is absorbed. Despite substantial advances in efficiency and cost, solar energy is still at least 5 to 10 times more expensive per kilowatt-hour than coal, gas, or oil.

- Recently, a new generation of photovoltaic cells based on nanoscale materials has received enormous attention because of its potential to dramatically reduce the cost of solar cell energy. These new opportunities arise from major advances in the ability to control the optical, electronic, and structural properties of materials at the nanometer scale.

- In addition, there are other ways in which nanotechnology could revolutionize solar cells. Because the most important function of a solar cell is to capture light, the ability to tune light absorption at the nanoscale could prove to be useful.

- In fact, scientists have already made solar cells out of quantum dots, which can be tuned to absorb different parts of the solar spectrum. This is an enormous advantage because solar cells are usually made with a given material, and often the material absorbs light efficiently only in one part of the spectrum but not others.

- Silicon, our most common solar cell today, is a material that absorbs light poorly over most of the solar spectrum. That means that it has to be made quite thick to have any chance at absorbing the rest of the spectrum, and because it has to be thick, it costs more money to be made much more electronically pure.

- By incorporating different sized quantum dots into a silicon solar cell, scientists have shown that we can greatly enhance the optical absorption efficiency of the material, possibly leading to much cheaper solar cells in the future.

- Another potential advantage of solar cells made from nanotechnology lies in the way in which the cells are manufactured. Quantum dots, for example, can be made using inexpensive, low-temperature, wet chemistry synthesis techniques.

- In addition, because nanotechnology-based cells can be ultrathin and still capture all of the light they need, these new solar cells could even be sprayed onto surfaces like paint, making them highly portable and extremely inexpensive to fabricate.

Nanotechnology and Health

- The areas of health and medicine may be where the largest and earliest impact of nanotechnology will be seen—the driving force being that biological structures are within the size scale that researchers are now able to manipulate and control: the nanoscale.

- For example, scientists are looking to nanotechnology to develop highly sensitive disease detectors as well as drug delivery systems that target the disease while sparing the surrounding healthy tissue.

- Many diseases do not exhibit recognizable symptoms until they are well advanced, but treatment is generally more effective if the disease is detected early. Nanoscale technologies are under development that will enable doctors to detect life-threatening diseases before they overwhelm the body.

- Sensors based on nanoscale materials have the potential to be millions of times more sensitive than their macroscale counterparts. They could also be designed to detect hundreds or even thousands of diseases at the same time.

- There are already some very promising sensors based on nanotechnologies that can be much smaller in size and have higher sensitivity than traditional sensors.

- In medicine, **biomarkers**, sensors that track the locations of things, are made using fluorescent dyes that are chemically modified to attach to whatever it is that you want to track. Biomarkers are enormously crucial to medical diagnostics.

- The use of dyes is tricky because they need to be excited by light of a certain wavelength in order for them to light up. Therefore, if you want to use different markers to track different biomolecules, you'd need a different dye each with its own light source.

- Quantum dots, on the other hand, are so small that they can go right into the cell membrane that they're tracking by attaching to the appropriate protein. In addition, just as the size-dependent color of quantum dots can be useful in solar cells, it can be game changing for the same reason in the field of medicine.

- Quantum dot sizes can be purposefully selected so that all different colors can be lit up with a single light source. A multi-colored, multi-functional map of what's going on inside the human body is now possible.

- In addition, unlike traditional dyes, quantum dots don't bleach out, which is a real problem in current medical imaging; instead, quantum dots keep going for as long as the imaging is needed.

- Another advantage of using quantum dots to track biomolecules is simply their size. Because quantum dots are smaller even than most proteins, they allow for much greater resolution of what's going on.

- Nanotechnology-based biomarkers are also being used to give a much more sensitive signal in detecting diseases. Researchers are also developing new kinds of nanoparticles that are meant to deliver drugs, heat, light, or other substances to specific types of cells, resulting in needing much lower doses of toxic chemicals and saving healthy tissue from damage.

- The use of nanotechnology in the field of medicine could revolutionize the way we detect and treat damage to the human body and disease in the future. Many techniques only imagined a few years ago are making remarkable progress toward becoming realities.

Nanotechnology and the Environment

- Nanotechnology is being explored for its potential to provide new solutions to managing and cleaning up pollution in our air, water, and land. There's a lot of cleaning we need to do, not just because of today's pollution, but much still needs to be cleaned up even from environmental messes we made long ago.

- Nanotechnology could provide cost-effective solutions to many challenging environmental cleanup problems. Researchers are currently working on developing nanoparticles that have the ability to detoxify a wide variety of common contaminants.

- One of the most abundant metals on Earth is pure iron. An ultrafine, nanoscale powder made from iron is turning out to be a remarkably effective way to clean up contaminated soil and groundwater.

- When iron particles are nanosized, they take on 2 enormous advantages: They become up to 1000 times more reactive than conventional iron powders because of the much larger surface area, and because they're so small, they can be incorporated into a slurry and pumped straight into the heart of a contaminated site.

- In the future, all existing industries are going to be improved and enabled with new applications because of nanotechnology. You'll be able to buy something that is made better—or just simply made in the first place—because it incorporates nanotechnology.

Important Term

biomarker: In medicine, this is a sensor that tracks the locations of things and is made using fluorescent dyes that are chemically modified to attach to whatever it is that needs to be tracked.

Suggested Reading

Allhoff, Lin, Moor, Weckert, and Roco, *Nanoethics*.

Garcia-Martinez and Moniz, *Nanotechnology for the Energy Challenge*.

Gratzel, *Nanotechnology*.

Shatkin, *Nanotechnology*.

Smith and Granqvist, *Green Nanotechnology*.

Questions to Consider

1. Think of something you like to do. Now think about how nanotechnology might change that in the future.

2. How did nature figure out how to make and use nanotechnology so efficiently, as in the case of the gecko?

Genetic Engineering—Life's Building Blocks
Lecture 10

In genetic engineering, we explore the most basic biological codes, the genetic codes, that govern life—the software of life. There is a common source code for life made with a basic set of commands that can be mixed and arranged in different ways to produce the most diversified set of life forms. There is a unifying underlying structure that allows for diversity as well as similarity, leading to many hugely important repercussions. Therefore, it's crucial to understand where and how the information of life is coded within the DNA itself.

Genomics and Genetic Engineering

- A molecule called DNA, or deoxyribonucleic acid, resides in every cell in a living form. DNA is responsible for the way we look, both inside and out, and the way in which our bodies from our feet to our brains function.

- DNA is what makes humans different from dogs, plants, or fish, and although those other forms of life are quite different than us, the same molecule exists at the core—a DNA, just with its individual components rearranged differently.

- Understanding the correlation between the arrangement of the components within DNA molecules and the features of a life form is called **genomics**.

- **Genetic engineering** is the ability to engineer life by accessing, modifying, and altering pieces of the inner source code of life itself.

- DNA is so small that it fits well into the realm of nanotechnology. Many consider DNA to be the single most advanced nanomaterial known. DNA is just a molecule, albeit a very complicated one, made of different components and elements.

- The famous double helix shape of the DNA molecule is crucial to its functionality. Each helix is a sequence of particular molecules that are attached to a spiraling backbone. Each of these molecules is connected to corresponding molecules in the other helix as they wind around one another.

- The pairing of these molecules along the winding strands and their ordering are what make up the bits of the source code. Hundreds of millions of these pairings make up the full DNA sequence, giving rise to the complete program.

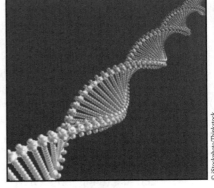

A molecule called DNA, deoxyribonucleic acid, is the source code of life; it resides in every cell in a living form.

- There are 4 molecules, which are called **bases**, that attach to the backbone of the DNA structure: adenine, cytosine, guanine, and thymine. When bonding across the strands in the helix, A pairs with T, and C fits with G—and vice versa.

- The key ingredient of genetic engineering is the fact that each submolecule of DNA (A, T, C, or G), or certain sequences of base pairs, can in principle be removed or modified.

- The precise sequence of components in the DNA is crucial because it corresponds to a particular functionality within the resulting organism. For example, it could be responsible for a particular protein, for a particular trait, or for a specific biological function. The segments of sequence that have a given function or purpose are called **genes**.

- Altering a sequence can alter the corresponding function, changing for example the way that DNA produces a particular protein. This could be highly desirable if such a modification were beneficial to our body, but we need to be very careful because a small change could also introduce a bug in our source code of life.

- Within the DNA molecule, we can identify different chunks with different functions. The most important ones are called **exons**, which make up only about 1.5% of the full DNA molecule. They're important because they are responsible for the production of proteins, which are the fuel that allows an organism to function.

- Proteins are the chief actors within the cell, carrying out the duties specified by the information encoded in genes. They are everywhere within the cell and in large quantities, often making up a much greater fraction of the cell than DNA.

- More than 95% of human DNA has large repeating sequences that appear to do nothing specific—sometimes called junk DNA or noncoding DNA. Scientists are trying to figure out what these sequences within the DNA actually do.

- Scientists think that the noncoding DNA could be responsible for gene regulatory expression, which means they regulate the behavior of specific organs and proteins, for example.

- These possibly wasteful segments of DNA are all the more interesting when we consider that more complex organisms have more of this noncoding DNA. Humans have by far the most. It's such an important mystery that it gets its own name in genetics: the C-value enigma.

- So far, we don't really understand how the size of the whole genome—the genes plus the noncoding segments—relates to the size and complexity of the organism. You might think that a larger genome would result in a bigger or more complex organism, but that is not the case, and we don't know why.

Gene Manipulation

- A gene is a segment of DNA that directs or codes for the production of a protein; proteins determine particular traits. For example, human eye color works in a way such that one person's genes produce proteins that make eyes brown while another person's genes produce proteins that make eyes blue.

- Other traits—like height and size in humans, or a plant's ability to withstand freezing temperatures—are more complex and may involve the interaction between a number of different genes, which produce the right proteins to generate these traits.

- Some genes have control regions that act like a light switch or a thermostat. They turn the gene on or off in order to regulate the amount of protein produced. This is simply because while cells carry identical DNA codes, different cells have different functions. We think that all the noncoding DNA in between the genes might be involved in these regulatory or switching functions.

- Even though it might seem pretty tough to pull out tiny sequences at exactly the right position out of chains hundreds of millions of units long, in some cases it's very simple. Typically, you can easily transfer DNA sequences of known effects and coding.

- More complex engineering can also be done. By modifying specific sections of DNA in bacteria, or in more sophisticated animals, we can get them to produce human proteins like insulin.

- The process is similar to a copy-and-paste procedure. The target DNA is cut at a particular location to expose 2 new endings where new sections of DNA will be attached. A temperature-controlled process will join these new parts to the original DNA. The new DNA is then ready for its new functions.

- The DNA is cut chemically by enzymes, which catalyze chemical reactions. That means that they make a chemical reaction occur that wouldn't ordinarily happen easily. Enzymes are usually highly specific and accelerate only one or a few chemical reactions in the cell. Proteins in the cell serve as enzymes.

- There are many thousands of varieties of enzymes, each able to recognize only one specific, tiny sequence in the DNA. Once it finds that sequence in a strand of DNA, it attacks it and splits the base pairs apart, leaving single helix strands at the end of the 2 double helixes. Scientists can then add any genetic sequences they want into the broken chain. Afterward, the chain is repaired with another enzyme called ligase. The organisms with DNA that have been modified in this way are called genetically modified organisms, or GMO.

- One major limitation is that we can only manipulate what we know about the DNA, which is very little; for humans, it's only about 1.5% of the DNA itself.

- There are 2 key challenges that scientists are working on today in genetic engineering: One is related to the full sequencing of the genome, and the other is related to understanding what each individual piece of genetic material actually does.

- The Human Genome Project has resulted in major improvements in the tools we use to generate and analyze enormous amounts of data. The full sequence of the human genome (about 3 billion base pairs and about 20,000–25,000 genes) was mapped by 2003.

- Sequencing the genome doesn't immediately lay open the genetic secrets of an entire species. Scientists are still trying to understand how the genome works—what the various genes that make up the genome do, how different genes are related, and how the various parts of the genome are coordinated.

- We haven't yet been able to exploit the full potential of genetic engineering. We need to be able to sequence as much DNA as possible to allow a cross comparison that would highlight what individual components of the DNA do.

- Major limitations include cost and time. It took $3 billion and many years of work to sequence one single DNA.

- The whole genome cannot be sequenced all at once because available methods of DNA sequencing can only handle short stretches of DNA at a time. Instead, scientists must break the genome into small pieces, sequence those pieces, and then reassemble them in the proper order to arrive at the sequence of the whole genome.

- We need game-changing advances in our sequencing. Exactly for this reason, and to encourage scientists to tackle this problem, in addition to government funding, a number of prizes and awards have been offered for new solutions.

The Biotech Revolution
- The biotech revolution started precisely around the idea that fast DNA sequencing would soon become available and affordable. In the 1980s, it was well known that such achievements could unlock the full potential of genomic engineering.

- If we could have a full genomic test that would cost the same as a blood test, we could design personalized medicine, in which treatment could be customized to each person's own genome. Not only would new genetically engineered cures become possible, but also current approaches to treating illness would become much more effective.

- People got quite excited about the potential benefits of genomics and genetic engineering in the 1980s. In addition to the possible medical benefits, many saw an enormous business opportunity.

- We have the potential for a revolution in biology and medicine based on genetic engineering that is similar if not even more transformational than what has happened in information technology. In electronics, the trick was due mainly to the miniaturization of components; in biotech, very different technologies are competing with each other. When that happens, progress is even faster.

- For genomics, in just 8 years, we have already moved from large research labs to tabletop sequencing units. We still don't have cheap genomic laptops, but we will not have to wait for long. In fact, maybe a disruptive genomic technology is right around the corner.

The Future of Genomics

- Today, we sequence DNA by reading the by-product of the DNA— namely, its proteins. It would be much easier if we could look directly at the DNA itself because it would allow us to skip the need to produce all those by-products, which is a very slow process.

- What the future holds, and what is being worked on in science labs across the world, is the ability to directly read DNA one genetic letter at a time. We would need to read 100s of millions of genetic letters in a row without making any mistakes.

- One of the reasons this vision is possible is thanks to nanotechnology. The key point is that we can make and control matter at the same size scale as the DNA molecule.

- There was some disappointment that the results of the Human Genome Project and the parallel research done in the private sector have not led to medical advances like personalized medicine more swiftly. Figuring out how the genes are regulated is far more difficult than simply sequencing them, as amazing a technical feat as that was.

Important Terms

base: One of 4 molecules that attach to the backbone of DNA: adenine, cytosine, guanine, and thymine. When bonding across the strands in the helix, A pairs with T, and C fits with G—and vice versa.

exon: A part of the DNA molecule that is responsible for the production of proteins but makes up only about 1.5% of the full DNA molecule.

gene: The segments of the DNA sequence that have a given function or purpose. The precise sequence of these components in the DNA is crucial because it corresponds to a particular functionality within the resulting organism.

genetic engineering: The ability to engineer life by accessing, modifying, and altering pieces of the inner source code of life itself.

genomics: The study of the correlation between the arrangement of the components within DNA molecules and the features of a life form.

Suggested Reading

Cummings, *Uncertain Peril*.

Nicholl, *An Introduction to Genetic Engineering*.

Shanks, *Human Genetic Engineering*.

Questions to Consider

1. What makes it so difficult to read DNA?

2. Once it's read, what's the main challenge to modifying it?

Synthetic Life—Making Life from Scratch
Lecture 11

In the last lecture, we learned about genetic engineering, which relates to how we can understand and engineer life at its very most basic building blocks. In this lecture, we'll talk not about modifying existing pieces of life, but rather about putting pieces together from scratch to make new kinds of life called synthetic life. Comparing DNA to the source code of a program, synthetic life is about writing new code from scratch to make life (that is, the program) do something new.

Creating Synthetic Life

- **Synthetic life** is the building of new life forms starting from nonliving substances. The goal in researching synthetic life is to engineer new forms of life that might be beneficial to our current global needs—in areas such as energy, water, and medicine.

- Synthetic biology aims to apply engineering (the art of making things, which implies taking parts and components and making something completely new) to biology, which aims to understand the inner workings of life in an organism—from the most fundamental components, such as base pairs in DNA, to the most complex components.

- There is a difference between modifying the genome and the idea of synthetic life. Blocks of code in the DNA correspond to specific functions. With synthetic life, on the other hand, the main idea is not to use a hosting form of life, but rather to take bits of DNA and make a completely new form of life out of them.

- Very recently, a new completely synthetic organism was put together using this approach. Researchers started by sequencing the genetic code of an existing bacterial genome, reading each and every base pair in order of the bacteria's DNA. Once they knew the exact sequence, the scientists were able to build that same DNA completely from scratch.

- The resulting cell for this first-ever case was pretty simple—and it took years of time and tens of millions of dollars in cost—although it's a remarkable demonstration of our ability to make and use DNA synthetically.

- If we want to make genetic code from scratch that is capable of constructing more complex forms of life, as in plants and animals, then even larger efforts will be needed.

- The rapid increase in our ability to make genetic code from scratch almost boggles the mind. Over the last 5 years alone, the field has seen a 100-fold increase in the length of genetic material that can be constructed entirely from raw chemicals.

- Synthetic life may in fact be a key to solving some of our most pressing current global challenges. For example, better decomposition processes by new synthetic forms of life can potentially increase the efficiency and yield of both biomass and biofuels.

- Any natural phenomenon that requires biological and chemical transformations can be sped up, for example, by the use of specialized bacteria that can perform very specific transformations. In other words, there is a whole world of potential biological transformations that is untapped because there is no form of life that can enact it.

Applications of Synthetic Life

- Synthetic life has many potential applications. For example, it could be used to design new and better pharmaceuticals and vaccines. Synthetic life may not only lead to the invention of new medicines and new cures, but also to improving the way our bodies react, at the molecular level, to the environment.

- Creating synthetic life could also work in applications outside of our body, for example, by developing bacteria that eat up oil spills or remove toxic contaminants like heavy metals and organic contamination in water wells and reservoirs. Building the DNA for such microorganisms from scratch, and tailoring them to do specific tasks and do them well, is certainly in the future of bioengineering.

- One could also use synthetic life in coordination with genetically modified food. Imagine that we change food to contain improved nutritional value but that collateral effects occur with that change: Synthetic life approaches could be used to introduce new bacteria that remediate any possible collateral effects induced by changing only parts of the DNA in food, allowing for greater tunability of the health benefits of the food in the first place.

- Synthetic life could be engineered to perform a variety of chemical reactions whose by-products would be new materials with new properties—for example, making materials with improved mechanical properties (new high-strength polymers) or materials with tailored optical and electronic properties.

- The merging of materials science with bioengineering and nanotechnology may be one of the most important developments over the next 50 years. Scientists have already been able to grow new materials by genetically engineering viruses.

- By constructing the DNA of the virus from scratch, we could open up a completely new, fully flexible way to design any material atom by atom. The enormous advantage is that, even though we can make really tiny things today, the operational scale of biological systems is still much smaller than the scale of our conventional manufacturing.

- Combining synthetic life with nanotechnology opens up the possibility to include inorganic—that is, nonliving—nanomaterials directly into living cells and organisms, for example, to improve our methods for enhancing new forms of synthetic life.

- In the future, synthetic life may not only be used to make new life, but also to improve it once it's made—without having to wait for generations. One could imagine engineering genetic biologic electronics, where natural and directed evolution would lead to a self-healing process that would ultimately result in a better electronic device.

- By integrating nanotechnology with biotechnologies, we may someday have biological nanosensors that are able to detect and interact with an environment to sense particular substances or, potentially, to correct issues or degeneration.

Ethical Issues

- Eventually, society as a whole will need to confront the ethical issues surrounding synthetic life. It will be extremely important for governments and lawmakers to make informed decisions about how to regulate the development of synthetic life forms.

- Many feel that, at least so far, what has been done with synthetic life is similar enough to what scientists have been doing in genomics for many years now—engineering the DNA of living organisms. However, like the atomic bomb, synthetic biology does pose practical risks.

- One concern is that someday the technology could be used to produce devastating biological weapons or that synthetic life forms could escape, mutate, and cause unforeseeable damage to the ecosystem.

- As with every technological advance since the wheel and fire, the ethical concerns surrounding synthetic biology rest not with the tool itself, but with the hand that wields it.

- Making synthetic life means more than simply replacing parts of living organisms with synthetic parts. The ultimate example of synthetic life would be to make from scratch a fully fledged human being. In principle, this is something we could do: In vitro processes are well established; the process of cloning is becoming more routine; and artificial DNA has already been made for microorganisms.

- If we can actually engineer a human through synthetic life, we will need to consider the many consequences: Once we have an optimal version of a person, should we clone it? Once the second version is out, what should we do with the first version? What is the best design for a human being? Who would even decide such a thing?

- Perfection and optimization are realized through evolution—through a continuous fine-tuning that has been going on for ages. If synthetic life is ever implemented for humans, it will use an evolutionary approach because that is what guarantees diversity and design improvements.

Synthetic life could be used to design new and better pharmaceuticals, among many other applications.

- In a way, synthetic life already exists; in fact, it has been the driver for the entire evolutionary process because evolution is the ultimate form of synthetic life. Starting with a few components, it created the seemingly magical and incredibly diverse ecosystem that we know today.

- The development of an organism is only partly determined by its genome; nongenetic factors play an important role as well. Therefore, even the best synthetically designed form of life will need to take into consideration the role of interactions with other beings and the environment it's in.

- If creating a human proves too controversial, could we use the technology to make spare parts? Robotics tries to do that with nonliving parts, but synthetic life technologies could potentially do the same with living parts. If we can replace broken parts, does that mean we can live forever?

Life without DNA

- On Earth, all life as we know it is based on DNA, the carbon-based molecule that contains the instructions for making and operating living cells in a 4-letter alphabet along its double-helix spine.

- Under the assumption that DNA is the basis for life, we could make synthetic life by using man-made chemicals to make up a DNA that we then would transfer to a host cell to allow its development either as a novel customized organism or as a completely new form of life.

- This process presumes that life itself can only happen through what we consider the model for natural life as we know it: We start with DNA (made of the 4 base molecules ATCG), which can reproduce itself and, through the help of a related molecule (RNA), can form complex proteins by assembling a combination of 20 amino acids according to the recipe that is in the DNA itself.

- Why not define a new synthetic life that is based on molecules other than ATCG? This crucial question of whether we can extend the concept of life to beyond DNA can be addressed by looking at what is going on at the frontiers of biotechnology.

- We usually think that living in a hostile environment is not easy and perhaps in some cases even impossible. Despite such hardship, we find that life can thrive in very harsh environments.

- Very recently, NASA scientists started to investigate the presence of bacterial life in the arsenic-rich waters of Mono Lake in California. The fact that bacterial life exists there is remarkable, but it's not as fascinating as the finding that the bacteria replaced phosphorous (which is essential to life as we know it) in their cellular composition with arsenic.

- In principle, one could think of making life out of silicon rather than carbon. While this is not necessarily possible, it's not something that we should discard as absurd. In addition, perhaps in the future we'll be able to use these forms of life to perform specialized jobs for us, benefitting from their ability to adapt to particular environments.

- In our search for extraterrestrial life, perhaps we should rethink what counts as a requirement for life. In fact, we may need to start thinking of life forms that don't use DNA at all.

- Very recently, scientists have invented a form of life that does away with DNA in which there is no double helix or base pairs involved—not all of them, anyway. Despite these absences, these "organisms" feed themselves and replicate themselves. In other words, it seems that DNA is not necessary for life.

- Changing the building blocks of life will enable revolutionary technologies as well as a better integration between living and nonliving organisms. It will also enable us to transcend our normal ways of thinking, bringing to the next level our search for life on Earth and beyond.

synthetic life: The building of new life forms starting from nonliving substances.

Suggested Reading

Rana, *Creating Life in the Lab.*

Regis, *What Is Life?*

Questions to Consider

1. Can we make life from genetic material different than what nature uses currently?

2. Do we need to start completely from scratch to consider something synthetic life? Where do we draw the line?

The Brain—Your Body's Supercomputer
Lecture 12

We know that our brain is the part of our body that makes us human, giving us the capacity for art, language, moral judgments, and rational thought. It's also responsible for our personality, memories, movements, and how we sense the world. When we look closely, we see in the brain an intricate network of wires, but we still have a hard time understanding the functions of the brain. For many tasks, the brain can outperform the fastest supercomputers on the planet, which can do trillions of mathematical operations per second.

Brain versus Computer

- The human brain is often compared to a computer. A computer is made mostly out of silicon while our brain is made predominantly out of organic materials based on carbon, but aside from the chemistry, their key functionalities are similar.

- In a computer, there is a computing chip (the central processing unit) and memory. Both a computer and the brain are made of a large network of individual components (transistors in the former and neurons in the latter), but neuroscientists have found that the brain is **plastic**—that is, it rewires itself over time, altering the strength of connections between neurons.

- There are many more neurons in the brain than there are transistors in any computer: We have about 100 billion neurons in our brain, and today's computer chips have about a billion transistors in them.

- A computer is a serial machine that processes instructions one after the next, so to be able to perform some operations, the computer needs to know the results of previous ones. This approach works in some tasks, but it falls short when the result of an operation can change if that of concurrent ones change as well.

- The brain is a massive parallel computer. The association of information done in parallel is used by the brain to connect completely different subjects. Complex operations such as image recognition or indexing personal memories are not serial processes, but parallel ones.

- The fastest computers today—called **supercomputers**—are designed to operate, at least in principle, similarly to a brain. They may have hundreds of thousands of processors in them connected by ultrafast networks. Not surprisingly, supercomputers have been pitted against a real set of human brains in various activities.

- While computers can perform specialized tasks exceptionally well today, they will not be able to do other things that the brain does equally well. That's not taking into account the size difference and power consumption of a supercomputer versus a brain.

The Evolution of the Brain

- The brains we have today have evolved immensely over millions of years. The size of our brains, measured by their total volume, has increased by more than a factor of 3 over the past 6 million years.

- While the brain did evolve considerably over this very long period of time, the brain that each one of us carries in our head is the result of major transformations, as we develop, that mimic that of the biological evolution of living organisms.

- There is enormous variety in the sizes and shapes of brains across the animal kingdom. However, if we divide the mass of the brain by the mass of the body, humans come out far ahead of any other animal.

- These transformations that occur in the development of the brain, or that result in these differences from one brain to another, are the result of evolution, which operates by adapting and changing DNA through mutations.

- Most research on the origin of the human brain has attempted to see what we have extra in our DNA that other animals do not have, but scientists have recently started looking at what genetic material we don't have.

- Although larger brain growth represents major evolutionary progress, we must also recognize that it came at huge costs. The brain consists of only 2% of our body weight and yet consumes up to 20% of the energy used by the human body—more than any other organ.

- In addition to this energy consumption, the brain in humans is also just plain large. Our brain-to-body-length ratio is about 1:8 for adults and 1:4 for infants.

What We Know about the Brain

- Today, we know that the brain is made of **neurons**—particular kinds of cells that exchange electric signals—but this is a fairly recent discovery.

- Brains were initially studied as we study any other organ—namely, by removal and dissection—but there was not a whole lot to be learned from this intricate jellylike organ using simple dissection.

- Instead, by associating the effects of damage of specific parts of the brain, early research was able to show that the brain has different regions within it that attend to different functions.

- The brain is basically a 3-pound mass of fat and protein that feels like jelly and has about 100 billion nerve cells known as neurons, which make up what is sometimes called the brain's gray matter because of their color.

- The neurons send and receive electrical signals that are transmitted via a network of millions of nerve fibers called dendrites and axons, which are known as the brain's white matter—again, because of their color.

- The cerebrum is the largest part of the brain, making up 85% of its total weight. The wrinkled outer surface is called the cerebral cortex, which is made up of gray matter, and underneath that is where the white matter is.

- The cerebrum is packed to maximum capacity inside our skulls, surrounding the rest of the brain, and deep folds allow it to cleverly maximize the cortex area. The cerebrum has 2 halves, which are further partitioned into 4 regions, or lobes, in each half.

- The frontal lobes, behind the forehead, are involved with speech, thought, learning, emotion, and movement. Behind them are the parietal lobes, which process sensory information such as touch, temperature, and pain. At the rear of the brain are the occipital lobes that deal with vision. The temporal lobes, near the temples, are involved with hearing and memory.

Studying the Brain

- Much of our understanding of the brain has come by investigating how particular environmental stimulations spark electrical signals throughout the brain. These stimulations are through our senses, such as looking at a familiar picture or remembering a thought.

- One of the simplest approaches is to place a bunch of probes around the outer shell of the brain (the cortex). To some extent, cerebral activity can be measured in response to such probes.

- **Electroencephalography (EEG)** is a way to detect the electrical activity of the brain. An EKG does the same thing for the heart. These measurements of electrical activity can be recorded from the outside of our skull or with much more detail when the probes are stuck into the cortex.

- We know that the brain is enormously complex, but we still have extremely primitive tools to measure and characterize this complexity. When we put probes around the outside of our skull, we are only measuring the signals that the brain gives off at the very exterior; there are many complex signaling patterns happening inside the brain that aren't detected with such probes.

- One approach that gets more information than a simple EEG is magnetic resonance imaging (MRI), which can scan a full cross section of the brain, and is noninvasive. These scans are relatively slow and require huge equipment, but because of the detailed information they provide about the brain's activity, they are becoming an indispensable tool for learning more about the brain.

- The ability for MRIs to read brain signals has important implications for future technologies that interface with the brain. One of the single greatest advances in brain science and technology will be new ways to read the neural activity inside the brain.

- We do have probes that go deeper into the brain. Basically, they are just very long, skinny needles. Probes can also be inserted specifically into regions of the brain we think are responsible for a certain illness, such as epilepsy, and electrical pulses delivered to these regions can help stop a seizure, for example.

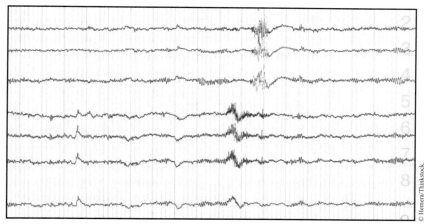

© Hemera/Thinkstock.

Electroencephalography (EEG) is used to measure the electrical activity of the brain.

- In the future, much better probes will be designed that are less invasive, allowing us to probe with greater accuracy the response of brain activity to stimuli.

- As in the case for DNA and genetic engineering, just getting the information is only a starting point; being able to acquire signals from the brain does not mean that we know how to interpret them.

- We need a sort of brain translator to decode these electrical signals. A greater understanding of the programming language our brain uses is what will be needed to complement the future advances in probes.

Brain Communication
- The nervous system is more than just the brain—it represents our body's full decision and communication center. The central nervous system consists of the brain and the spinal cord; the peripheral nervous system is made of nerves, all of which have neurons firing electrical signals among them.

- Nerves extend from your brain to your face, ears, eyes, nose, and spinal cord, and from the spinal cord to the rest of your body. Sensory nerves are designed to gather information from the environment and then send that information to the spinal cord, which acts as a superhighway to speed up the message and get it to the brain.

- The brain then makes sense of that message and sends out a response. Motor neurons are named as such because they are the ones that deliver the instructions from the brain to the rest of your body.

- Pain is a communication to the brain that there is something wrong; it is essentially an error message, which in a computer usually means that some action needs to be taken to mitigate a problem.

- Sometimes we can even have pain when there really is no peripheral that creates the problem. This is called **virtual pain**, and it is a very common phenomenon among recent amputees. This is a normal reaction mechanism of the brain as it keeps trying to exchange messages to and from a missing part of the body.

- The possibility of creating artificial prosthetics that can actually send and receive neural signals—thereby having the ability to exchange information with the brain—may become a reality in the future.

Limits of the Brain

- Just like with a computer, there is a limit to everything. In principle, a brain could and probably should adapt to overstimulation, but because the hardware is what it is, at least in this era of evolution, performance may suffer.

- The brain needs a maintenance mode to be able to rest itself, to consolidate its data—it's called sleep, which is essential for the brain. It allows for a rewiring of lost or damaged neural connections, and it consolidates the data acquired throughout the day.

- If we could understand and learn the language of our brain and of our neural networks, then maybe someday we could even write our own computer codes in the same language our brain uses.

- The same neurological mathematical algorithms used by the brain—once we understand them—could change the paradigm of how we use computers.

- So far, we still don't even know what makes us conscious beings. Unlike the more specific functions, scientists have not been able to identify consciousness with any particular section of the brain.

- Understanding how the brain relates to consciousness will be just as important as getting a grip on those algorithms and programming languages. In the future, we will know much more about consciousness and what it means to be human.

Important Terms

electroencephalography (EEG): A way to detect the electrical activity of the brain in which measurements of electrical activity can be recorded from the outside of the skull.

neuron: A particular kind of cell in the brain that exchanges electric signals.

plastic: In terms of neuroscience, this is the notion that the brain rewires itself over time, altering the strength of connections between neurons.

supercomputer: A computer designed to operate, at least in principle, similarly to a brain that is the fastest type of computer currently used. It may contain hundreds of thousands of processors connected by ultrafast networks.

virtual pain: A common phenomenon among recent amputees that is a normal reaction mechanism of the brain as it keeps trying to exchange messages to and from a missing part of the body.

Suggested Reading

Bear, Connors, and Paradiso, *Neuroscience*.

Buzsaki, *Rhythms of the Brain*.

Restak, *The Secret Life of the Brain*.

Simon, *The Brain*.

1. How much do we actually know about the brain? Why is it so complicated?

2. What is learning, and how is it related to pattern recognition?

Cancer and Aging—Can They Be Defeated?
Lecture 13

The question of whether we can live forever depends on coming to understand what is going on in our cells and how to control the processes that occur. In this lecture, we'll learn about the life and death of a cell and how this relates to 2 of the greatest—and, not coincidentally, related—health questions of our time: when and how we will cure cancer and how long we can ultimately live. The answer to both of these questions begins with an understanding of what the cell is and how it works.

Cell Basics

- Cells are the basic unit of structure and function in living things, the smallest things that can perform all of the functions of life. Most cells are very small and can't be seen without magnification. As a result, our knowledge of cells has grown only as technology has allowed us to see them.

- All life on Earth can be divided into 2 categories: **eukaryotes** and **prokaryotes**. The cells of a eukaryote are complex and contain a nucleus and other membrane-bound structures. Eukaryotes include animals, plants, protists, and fungi. With the exception of protists and the yeasts, which are single-celled fungi, all eukaryotes are multicellular.

- Prokaryotes, or bacteria, are much simpler in structure. These cells have no internal membranes. These simple prokaryotes colonized Earth 2 billion years before eukaryotes ever showed up on the scene.

- Eukaryotic cells come in a wide variety of shapes and sizes because they all perform different functions, but most cells are quite tiny, and this has to do with simple geometry more than anything else.

- Some cells can live independently of other cells. These are unicellular organisms and can grow, feed, reproduce, and breathe completely on their own. It is remarkable how much these animals, which don't have nervous systems, have recognizably animallike behavior. Systems inside the cell compute what ought to be done next.

- Other cells are highly specialized and can function only in association with many others as part of a multicellular organism.

Cancer Basics

- Today, cancer is responsible for the death of 17% of the world's population. The disease manifests itself as uncontrolled cell growth.

- In cancer, normally functioning cells are replaced by fast-replicating malignant cells, which lose the functionality they once had. These malignant cells attack neighboring cells and have the potential to spread across organs and the body—through the circulatory and immune systems.

- What makes cancer so deadly is that even once it's eradicated from one spot in the body, it has the ability to metastasize, or resurface, in other parts of the body and often with a much greater degree of severity. Benign tumors, by contrast, also show cellular overgrowth, but they do not spread and can be contained or surgically removed.

- Because cancer has the ability to travel and metastasize across the body, sometimes very quickly, detecting the presence of cancer as early as possible through screening is of paramount importance for a successful fight against the disease.

- Cancer is essentially a genetic disease or, rather, set of diseases. It turns out that a normal cell can quite frequently undergo a mutation in its DNA due to a number of different possible factors.

- A natural process of genetic error correction in the body usually suppresses the damaged cell, but sometimes the mutation affects the particular section of the DNA that is responsible for the repair of the DNA when it gets damaged.

- The mutation first inactivates what is called a tumor suppressor gene, which suppresses the cell cycle or even promotes **apoptosis**, which is the so-called programmed cell death that all cells have. Between 50 and 70 billion cells in your body die every single day because of apoptosis.

- Without apoptosis, our bodies wouldn't even grow. Programmed cell death is something we are still learning about, but we know for sure that an error in this crucial function—for example, if it is turned off—is what happens in cancer.

- Without such a self-correcting mechanism, the cell is free to do whatever it wants. Nothing will terminate it. When a mutation inactivates several tumor suppressor genes, cancerous cells start their uncontrolled growth. Because they usually are damaged by mutation, these cells also lose the functionality of the original cell.

- Cancerous cells, just like any cell or virus, use evolution to improve themselves. If the initial mutations that lead to the formation of the first cancerous cells are fairly mild, the body may not recognize any threat, and evolution can tend to emphasize those traits. A chain reaction of further mutations will actually be favored by the body, making subsequent generations of cancer cells more dangerous and faster spreading.

- Ultimately, they become so invasive that they cross organ boundaries and attack pretty much anything in the body. The key, even for the cure, is to pay particular attention to what causes the first mutations in the normal cell that removes control over normal tissue growth.

Causes of Cancer
- Genetic traits can create a predisposition to cancer. Some cells will be more susceptible to mutate in some individuals. However,

genetic causes account for only about 5% of the occurrences of cancer today. The remaining ones are due to environmental factors.

- The combination of diet, physical inactivity, and obesity has an enormous impact on your risk of getting cancer. Some foods contain **carcinogens**, which are things that can cause a cell to become cancerous. Carcinogens can creep unnoticed into one's daily food by insecticides, growth hormones, and preservatives—or they could simply occur naturally in the food itself.

- The combination of a high-calorie, high-salt diet with little physical activity and obesity act to decrease the ability of the body to cure itself from possible cancerous cells. Issues that occur as a result in the immune and circulatory systems don't provide a healthy environment for your cells.

- Not all of the different chemical substances that are related to cancer act in the formation of cancer in the same way. Some are mutagens, such as tobacco or sunlight, where the substance or radiation directly stimulates the DNA to mutate.

Asbestos was formerly widely used in building materials but was banned after asbestos fibers were found to be harmful when inhaled.

- Tobacco causes 30% of all cancer cases today. Tobacco smoke contains over 4000 chemical compounds, many of which are carcinogenic or otherwise toxic. That is why many tobacco smokers develop lung cancer.

- A class of nonmutagens also exists. They do not stimulate mutations but, rather, only the growth of existing cancer cells. Excessive alcohol consumption is one example, but excessive food consumption, or unhealthy food, is another one.

- Among mutagen agents, radiation can be a significant contributor to cancer, but not all radiation is dangerous or carcinogenic. The kind of radiation to worry about is called ionizing radiation because exposure to it induces ionization in the atoms in your DNA, which can cause mutations.

- Radioactivity is the most common form of ionizing radiation, but lasers and X-rays are other examples. Sunlight can also be considered an ionizing radiation source and, in particular, the ultraviolet part of the spectrum. Excessive exposure to UV rays can lead to aggressive forms of cancers.

- Radioactive poisoning, which essentially means being exposed to more than the normal levels of radiation, can happen directly through inhalation or ingestion of radioactive material or indirectly through consumption of contaminated food and water.

- The majority of radiation-induced cancers are due to radon contamination. Radon is a radioactive element that can be found in the ground. Usually, ventilation and natural agents dilute this dangerous gas sufficiently to render it harmless, although there are conditions where accumulation of radon is possible and dangerous levels can be reached.

- When inhaled in significant quantities, the bioaccumulation of asbestos as a foreign material is ultimately responsible for the development of cancer in the lungs and in their protective linings.

- Research suggests that hormones can also act as cancer stimulators. High exposure to hormones naturally enhances the performance of particular organs, but while such substances are generated by the body to improve the performance of good cells, they also have the potential to enhance the performance of cancer cells.

Future Cures for Cancer

- Today's methods to cure cancer typically rely on invasive surgeries to remove cancerous cells or organs. Often in addition, potent chemicals and radiation are used separately or together to kill and reduce the amount of cancerous cells. These methods very often either miss parts of the cancer or cause damage to a lot of the healthy tissue, having highly adverse effects.

- In the future, we will rely on much more focused, smart, and localized approaches. Using specifically designed nanomaterials, we will be able to deliver medicine only to the region affected by the cancer, leaving undisturbed the unaffected surrounding cells.

- Because cancer is a disease that starts at the level of the DNA, a much deeper understanding of the DNA will allow us to design better genetic drugs, ones that can directly fight against the initial stages where the mutations first happen.

- More detailed information about our genetic makeup will also allow doctors to identify with greater accuracy potential hereditary genes that are precursors to cancer. With this knowledge, using genetic engineering, in the future we might even be able to deploy a cure before the cancer has actually manifested.

- Genetically modified viruses may provide the means to rapidly scan cells—picking out healthy versus cancerous ones—and correct the errors due to mutations that may ultimately lead to cancer.

- In the future, we will be engineering viruses to provide cures for many diseases. Unfortunately, as new materials and technologies evolve, new forms of diseases and types of cancers will most certainly appear.

- In one possible future scenario, we may be able to develop treatments—perhaps based on nanotechnology—that are able to repair, at the cellular or molecular level, anything that goes wrong before it manifests itself as a noticeable problem.

The Science of Aging

- Until around 20 years ago, scientists used to think that aging was fixed—a process programmed into our biology that resulted in a built-in time of death. Some scientists now believe that one day humans could live to be 300 or even 400 years old.

- One of the key issues to reaching such a future is that we are up against evolution itself. A biological system that lived forever would be very hard for evolution to produce because perfect repair mechanisms would have to be much more sophisticated and, therefore, much less likely to evolve.

- More importantly, perfect repair mechanisms are unnecessary. In order for evolution to work, we just need to live long enough to have offspring. There is no natural selection favoring longer lifespan.

- There is no programmed limit to lifespan as we once thought. Aging is extremely complicated: It affects the body at all levels, and it involves many different kinds of molecular and cellular damage. We need to know the nature of the molecular defects that drive the aging process at the cellular level.

- In the future, we will gain a much deeper understanding of what is going on at the molecular level within our cells, the hundreds of genes responsible for all the intricate processes that carry out cellular maintenance and repair. As we learn more about these functions and learn how to control them, the potential health benefits will extend far beyond cancer and aging.

apoptosis: The programmed cell death that all cells have. Between 50 and 70 billion cells in a human body die every day because of apoptosis.

carcinogen: Something that can cause a cell to become cancerous.

eukaryote: Mostly multicellular organisms having complex cells that contain a nucleus and other membrane-bound structures. Eukaryotes include animals, plants, protists, and fungi.

prokaryote: Bacteria that is much simpler in structure than a eukaryote. These cells have no internal membranes and colonized Earth 2 billion years before eukaryotes existed.

Suggested Reading

Brown, *The Living End.*

Kleinsmith, *Principles of Cancer Biology.*

Olshansky and Carnes, *The Quest for Immortality.*

Weinberg, *The Biology of Cancer.*

Questions to Consider

1. What's happening inside a cancer cell to make it so deadly?

2. What determines our life expectancy? What's the role of the environment as opposed to the cell's metaphorical clock in aging?

Powerful Viruses—Future Friend or Foe?
Lecture 14

S cary diseases have long been a staple of science fiction, but in recent years, they've come to seem all too real. Some viral diseases are as mild as the common cold; some are life threatening. Some are transmitted through close contact; some can attack us through the air. We know how to prevent some, but not others. The vast majority of viruses actually does a lot of good and is essential to life on Earth. Future medicine, biology, and nanotechnology will make use of viruses to change the way we live.

Viruses versus Bacteria

- The major difference between viruses and bacteria is simply in their dimensions. A bacterium is about 500 (and up) nm across, and it is usually a **monocellular** organism—that is, an organism made of just one cell. A virus is much smaller. In fact, the smallest viruses are barely bigger than DNA itself, which is just a few nanometers across.

- Essentially, a bacterium is the most basic form of life. It can live by itself, and it has its own DNA. Although it was once thought to be, a virus is not a living organism, for 2 key reasons: It doesn't have a cellular structure, and it doesn't have its own metabolism.

- To be able to survive, a virus needs a hosting cell; it's basically a complex parasite. A virus does not contain any cells, but it does have genetic material. In fact, besides a little bit of fat and a complex surface, we can say that a virus is basically all DNA or RNA.

- One very important aspect of a virus is its surface. While a cell is fairly uniform, a virus has a very rough, complex surface. This monstrous aspect is due to the presence of the so-called attachment complexes and insertion complexes, which are crucial for the virus's survival.

- The DNA of a virus is complex and, to some extent, similar to that of living organisms. However, in contrast to bacteria and any regular living organisms (human beings included), the virus cannot reproduce by cell division—where the DNA unfolds, replicates, and the cell splits.

- The only possible mechanism for a virus to reproduce is through self-assembly. Basically, it uses a host to replicate and clones itself piece by piece. This is what makes viruses interesting and extremely powerful.

- In the process of replicating itself, the DNA material doesn't necessarily have to remain the same, but it can change through genetic mutations in this sense just like a regular living organism. It is indeed because of this that viruses can be extremely dangerous.

© Comstock/Thinkstock.

When a Virus Attacks

- Because a virus requires self-assembly for its replication, such a process requires a host cell where this replication can take place. It's essential for the virus to have an easy way to attach itself to the host cell. This is what the attachment complexes on the surface of the virus are for.

When a cell is infected with HIV, the genetic material of the virus becomes part of the genetic code of the hosting cell.

- After the rendezvous with the host cell, the genetic material of the virus (DNA or RNA, depending on the type of virus) is injected in the hosting cell through the insertion complex on the virus's surface. Once the genetic material is inside the cell, the takeover begins.

- The genetic material of the virus becomes surrounded on all sides by the DNA of the hosting cell, and it literally becomes part of the genetic code of the hosting cell. The modified DNA then starts to produce copies of the viral RNA and DNA, making multiple copies within the cell itself.

- These DNA copies are then surrounded by a membrane and eventually expelled from the host cell in large quantities and, most importantly, in the same exact form as the initial attacking virus: a single strand of genetic code encased within a protein capsule.

- If we define life by the ability to move a genetic blueprint into future generations, then viruses would have to be classified as alive. They are undeniably the most efficient entities on this planet at propagating their genetic information. Scientists sometimes discuss viruses as somewhere in between living and nonliving.

Vaccines and Antiviral Drugs

- The needs for various vaccines are proportional to the level of danger associated with a particular virus. Because the process is so invasive—and because of the very dynamic, mutating nature of a virus—the development of vaccines is of paramount importance.

- Apart from vaccines, which basically prevent us from getting infected, there is a lot of work going on to develop **antiviral drugs** that fight the infection of a virus. Because viruses cannot reproduce without infecting a host cell, antiviral drugs are designed to interfere with the infection process.

- Antiviral drugs hijack the virus with some bits of fake DNA that do 1 of 3 things: disable the attachment ability of the modified virus so that it is no longer able to connect with its host cell; modify the virus's ability to inject its own DNA into the host; or prevent the virus from leaving the hosting cell, causing infection.

- While antiviral drugs have demonstrated some effectiveness for certain viruses, so far the best cure is still prevention, and this means that the appropriate vaccine is the best way to remain virus free.

- In essence, the vaccine teaches the body about a particular foreign virus and prepares it through the immune system to be ready in case of an infection. If the body then enters into contact with the virus, this is immediately recognized, and destroyed, before it has a chance to spread by creating endless copies of itself.

- The lesson that the vaccine teaches to the body must be customized to a particular virus. The best way to do this is to use the original virus itself. The vaccine, therefore, is nothing more than the genetic material of the virus itself that has been deactivated. That way, the body builds up its virus-fighting army without having a real war.

- Because vaccines are designed and only work for one specific virus and because there are many different viruses, a universal vaccine seems to be a possible solution. We would be able to have a universal vaccine if we would have only a very small set of never-changing viruses, which is unfortunately not the case.

- Viruses, in typical evolutionary fashion, evolve to survive. As soon as they cannot find a viable way to reproduce—say, because of vaccines—then they mutate, or change little bits of their DNA, in a way that allows them to overcome the vaccines and spread again.

- For people who make vaccines, it's always a matter of chasing the latest virus, catching it, and containing it. If we knew in advance what mutations would come next, we would be able to prevent the formation of novel viruses. Unfortunately, we still don't have such a capability.

The Evolution of Viruses
- The evolutionary process of viruses is extremely interesting. We might think that mutations are achieved through small modifications until the virus has become different enough to be able to infect and reproduce again, but sometimes successful mutations happen when

a virus attacks a particular animal and then mutates to attack a different animal.

- Mutation for viruses is a matter of survival. Unfortunately for us, this indicates how smart a virus can be. To be able to control and defeat a virus is a race against time.

- Some viruses are much easier to transmit than others. The faster and easier the transmission, the less time we have until we get to the point of an epidemic or, worse still, a pandemic. While epidemics used to be confined, pandemics are potentially a lot easier to develop today.

- Modern times actually make the virus's job a lot easier, as viruses can be easily spread across nations and continents through jet travel. On the upside, as soon as an outbreak develops, the whole world can, in principle, find the proper vaccine for it.

Fighting Viruses in the Future
- The very basic principle of vaccines, and the way they are prepared, will most likely remain the same in the future. What will change is the ability to quickly recognize the virus, decode its DNA, and synthetically prepare the vaccine.

- A portable device could be used to make custom vaccines starting from the DNA of the virus, ready in a matter of minutes. Such a device would be able to quickly read the hundreds of millions of pieces of genetic material that make up the virus and then do the chemistry needed to modify those bits of the virus's DNA that will make it harmless.

- In the future, not only will we need very fast ways to sequence DNA, we'll also need to have new synthetic chemistry capabilities to create vaccines from scratch that do not rely on the actual virus itself, as we do today.

- Many viral pandemics have crossed human history, such as the bubonic plague, with devastating effects. These pandemics occurred not only because people didn't have the tools to make the right vaccinations and antiviral drugs; it had just as much to do with a fundamental lack of understanding of the biological world.

- You may think that a goal for the future would be to remove all of the bad viruses in the world, but in fact, we would not want to do that. Despite the fact that some viruses are quite deadly, some other viruses can actually do a lot of good.

- The natural and continuous way viruses evolve and adapt to an environment is actually crucial for life itself. For example, viruses are what regulate life in aquatic environments. Without viruses, bacteria could develop in seas and oceans and quickly destroy vegetation and fish.

- Although viruses are not life per se, they are the main regulatory entities that allow for a critical balance in life. They not only kill potentially devastating predators, but they also regulate the way biomass is regenerated, in particular through algal growth.

- In addition to regulating life in aquatic environments, viruses also play a significant role as one of the major vehicles to evolution. They enhance the ability to transfer genes between different species, which increases overall genetic diversity and drives evolution.

- Learning more about the genetic diversity of viruses in the future could lead to a deeper understanding of the role of viruses in evolution and, most importantly, how to use custom-made viruses to our benefit.

- By taking advantage of the way viruses interact at the level of the DNA within an organism, we could think in the future of using viruses to correct errors within the DNA of the hosting organism.

- Viruses could then be the vehicle for cures of genetic diseases, possibly including cancer. By using viruses, one could restore the DNA of cancerous cells to the premutation stage, which would make them die naturally and noninvasively.

- Furthermore, viruses are small and smart but can be made even smarter or simply more useful when combined with other tools, such as nanotechnology. Because the size of a virus is in the nanometer range, we can imagine in the future integrating nanomaterials directly with viruses.

- In addition, completely new materials could be made at the atomic scale using viruses as the design and assembly engine. The result might be devices made from cheaper, abundant, and nontoxic materials that are built from the DNA up by the common virus.

Important Terms

antiviral drug: A drug that fights the infection of a virus.

monocellular: An organism made of just one cell.

Suggested Reading

Biskup and Derington, *Understanding Viruses with Max Axiom*.

Kolata, *Flu*.

Mnookin, *The Panic Virus*.

Shors, *Understanding Viruses*.

1. At the edge of life, viruses are not quite considered living organisms. Why not?

2. Are viruses really all bad? Give an example of how we may use them in the future to save the world.

Food or Famine—Science Holds the Key
Lecture 15

Food is the power—the fuel—behind our life. Food is very complex and has been dramatically changed over the years by science and technology. In this lecture, we'll discuss the major advances in improving our food—although in some cases, at a cost—and we'll discuss how science and technology will bring the next generation of food to our tables. In the future, our food may be genetically modified or even virtual. Regardless, we'll never stop seeking to maintain the pleasures of consuming food, smelling its aromas, and tasting its delicious flavors.

Food as Energy

- Basically, food is simply a form of energy. It is an energy currency among all living organisms. A joule is one of the most common units for measuring energy, and one joule is roughly equal to the amount of energy your body releases as heat every $1/60^{th}$ of a second.

- The more complex the organism, the more energy it requires. In fact, the more we go up the food chain, the less efficient our food resource becomes because only a fraction of the energy available at one level of the food chain is transferred to the next level—with an average of only about 10%.

- Because more advanced animals require more energy, they use the less complex plants and animals as their source of food, which in turn use less complex animals, and so forth. There are really only 2 living organisms that eat everything at all scales in the food pyramid: humans and decomposing bacteria. Because of this, for humans, food is a highly complex issue and a very diversified material.

- Because we're not designed to process too much energy at a time, we would not want to always eat foods with the highest energy densities; our digestive systems simply could not handle it. Therefore, a balance is required because complex chemical reactions are taking place to break down and utilize the energy stored in food.

The ability to make vegetables and fruit last longer is a genetic modification that will become important in the future.

- Geography is another factor that affects food: Where you live determines what you eat. Historically, there were pockets around the world with lots of foods that gave a strong basis for human evolution, and indeed, societies formed around them, dating back to the first known civilization in Mesopotamia.

- Science has changed this dynamic. Major advances in transportation have allowed for food to become a global fuel rather than a local one. This is a direct result of scientific advances having an enormous impact on the way we eat and, therefore, the way we live.

Food Preservation

- Globalized food can only be achieved even today with proper ways of packaging and preserving the food. This is accomplished by making sure the food is not exposed to what are called oxidizing agents—these are basically humidity or water—which lead to the food spoiling.

- From canned or vacuum-pressed food to refrigerators, there is a whole array of technologies available to maintain food— that is, to keep it edible for as long as possible. The technology behind food preservation through optimal packaging has evolved tremendously in the last decades, and the spoiling of food has been significantly reduced.

- Freezing is an effective form of food preservation because the pathogens that cause food spoilage are either killed or don't grow very rapidly at reduced temperatures. However, freezing is actually less effective than heating because pathogens are more likely to be able to survive cold rather than hot temperatures.

- One of the problems with the use of freezing as a method of food preservation is the danger that pathogens become deactivated but not killed by the process and will become active again when the frozen food thaws.

- Foods can be preserved for several months by freezing, but if you want to store food for that long, it requires a constant temperature of −18°C (0°F) or less. Some freezers can't reach such low temperatures on a consistent basis. Temperature fluctuations in your freezer can also occur simply by adding a bunch of new, unfrozen food to it.

- Food can also be preserved chemically through what we know as food preservatives and additives. While many of the preservatives pose little short-term threats to health—and the benefits far outweigh the risks—the long-term effects are not necessarily known, and preservatives have been associated with several diseases.

- Artificial or natural chemicals (the boundaries aren't always clear) can be added to food not only to help in their preservation, but also to enhance flavor, taste, and appearance.

Genetically Engineering Food

- The space race of the 1960s made us believe that in the future all food would be processed and efficiently packaged—and then automatically cooked. Such futuristic expectations didn't quite translate to today.

- Such food is not very tasty, but it's also not very healthy. In fact, society is now moving toward a return to unprocessed foods, simply and naturally cooked.

- It's not just a health issue, but also a social change. Cooking is popular again, and paying attention to the details beyond taste—such as visual aspects or texture—is assuming an increasingly important role.

- Science was key to this transition and helped us move forward by returning to older practices. Today, we know pretty much almost everything that is in our food, from chemicals to nutrients.

- Food manufacturers would love to be able to make cooking into something objective, where every detail is measured and optimized to suit consumer preferences. In order to replicate a recipe, and the secret taste sensations therein, every single detail has to be tested objectively. The problem is that some of the sensors we use for this are not objective: our tongues and noses.

- As part of having a more scientific approach to cooking, we will see in the future the development of artificial tongues and artificial noses, able to understand and quantify a particular flavor.

- Why should we only settle with what nature provides us? Can we change ingredients at their core molecular level to give us any taste or even function to the food itself? These possibilities come into focus by genetically engineering food.

- The process of genetic engineering has been done for millennia as an early form of applying scientific understanding to the development of new food—namely, connecting color to taste and nutrition—by selecting favorable qualities to breed.

- Another way we can change food that was already discussed is by selecting certain aspects of the DNA itself and modifying the DNA, which results in **genetically modified food (GMF)**. Even if we could do this kind of DNA engineering, it's not clear that it would be advantageous.

- In the case of the early form of genetic engineering, we relied on evolution and guided evolution to keep selecting the strongest or particular preferred varieties. In the case of GMF, we artificially implant sections of chemistry into the DNA of the plant or animal that leads to a change in the genetics, resulting in different characteristics.

- This new kind of GMF has a very short history; it was only first successful in the 1980s when a new kind of vegetable oil was engineered. Much more recently, animals have also been genetically modified.

- Another important driver behind the genetic modification of plants was the desire to make them resistant to certain pesticides. This allows for the use of pesticides that might have killed the naturally occurring form of the plant. However, the consequences of using stronger pesticides for the environment—including humans—are hard to predict.

- Another genetic modification that will become important in the future is the ability to make vegetables and fruit last longer—that is, not decompose as quickly. So far, however, this approach has been met with challenges because the same modifications that make it last longer also change the taste.

- In the future, genetically modified food could be used as a vehicle for large-scale immunization against diseases. It could also be used to mitigate the allergenic effects of particular types of food by removing the allergenic components while retaining the other crucial nutrients in those foods.

- Perhaps one of the most important future uses of GMF will be to add helpful nutrients into food. Recently, scientists have been able to add vitamin A into rice and corn. This will be an enormous help, in particular to parts of the world where there are serious health issues related to lack of nutrition.

- GMF has many different potential applications, and it is also a growing direction for our food. Almost all soybeans planted today have already been genetically modified. This trend toward genetic modification will certainly continue for other foods in the future.

- With science and technology, there are always risks that may be involved. In the case of GMF, these risks are still heavily debated, despite the fact that the FDA has approved genetically modified food as a safe food.

- With GMF, there could be the risk of a potential reduction in the number and diversity of species. This concern has not yet been significantly investigated due to the fact that the large-scale adoption of GMF is fairly recent.

- Despite the cautions, GMF has the potential for a significant improvement in the food itself and of the means we use to grow it. Besides improving yield, there is a lot of potential to add nutritional capabilities to a particular food—either in terms of the energy it produces or as supplemental components such as vitamins or iodine.

- In addition, if we could make food more pest resistant—as opposed to pesticide resistant—it would lead to a reduction in the use of dangerous pesticides and herbicides, which would be a huge benefit to the environment as well as a reduction in the actual cost.

Food in the Future
- Earth's temperature is rising, reducing the amount of available land to cultivate, and the world population is projected to keep steadily increasing. In other words, the world is getting busier with people in need of food, but the amount of natural resources—and in particular, sources of food and water—is going to be in decline.

- In addition to enhancing our efforts on conservation of resources, we also need to be smart and use science and technology to engineer food that will allow us to feed the world. The future of GMF will play a very crucial role in this challenge by allowing us to produce food with higher energy density so that we can feed a higher number of people from the same amount of land.

- In the future, we will certainly be using genetic engineering to make food taste better. We will most likely understand and quantify the origin of a flavor through artificial noses and tongues and, from there, relate it to the actual DNA or the exact chemical composition of a particular food. With this powerful knowledge, we will be able to alter food genetically, to adapt its taste, and to change the consistency, texture, and appearance.

- In the future, perhaps we will be able to have virtual food. With a set of noninvasive electrodes in the mouth, and a nose embedded in a soft matrix, we will be able to chew on something and get the exact flavor that we want. People will be able to enjoy certain forbidden foods only because the brain will be tricked into thinking they are having that food. Texture will be reproduced too, using materials that can change consistency on demand.

Important Term

genetically modified food (GMF): A hypothetical way to change food by selecting certain aspects of the DNA itself and modifying the DNA.

Suggested Reading

Canavari and Olson, *Organic Food*.

Jango-Cohen, *The History of Food*.

Nestle, *Food Politics*.

Questions to Consider

1. What is genetically modified food, and why do we modify it?

2. How has packaging and conservation of food changed the way we eat—and, therefore, live?

Water—The Currency of the Next Century
Lecture 16

Water is the most precious thing we have on this planet, and it's what makes life possible. We sometimes take it for granted—well, we always take it for granted—but we shouldn't. In fact, it's so precious and becoming so scarce in so many places around the world that, soon, many people will likely start trading it like a currency. In this lecture, we'll find out why the currency of the next century might be water and how science can possibly help in alleviating this scarcity.

Earth's Water

- Water is essential to life. A large portion of every living organism is made of plain water; 75% of what we humans are is water. Water is what carries and distributes nutrients and oxygen throughout our body, and it's also a means for removing waste and toxins.

- Primordial and simple life forms like bacteria can only survive in aqueous solutions, so to maintain life, we need to supplement it either directly with water or with the water that's in nutrients and food. In addition, we need water to make that food—to grow vegetables or farm animals.

- Water is one of the most atypical liquids. No other common material is found in all 3 phases (liquid, solid, and gas). It has an unusually high melting point, boiling point, surface tension, viscosity, and it expands upon freezing—unlike almost every other liquid.

- The density of ice is lower than the density of water. The freezing of rivers, lakes and oceans is from the top down for the same reason because ice floats. This permits the survival of the bottom ecology because the ice insulates the water from further freezing and reflecting back sunlight.

- Earth can be divided up into roughly 2/3 water and 1/3 land, but almost all of that water is seawater, which at least in its original form is completely useless to us as drinking water. Freshwater is what we need, and there's very little of it on the planet. Out of all of Earth's water, only 2.5% of it is freshwater.

- Through the water cycle, the small amount of freshwater we have is continuously used and regenerated. Evaporation from the oceans allows for condensation into clouds and precipitations as snow and rain. This water is collected either in groundwater reservoirs or in rivers and lakes. Nature uses this system to allow life to take place.

- There are an increasing number of places around the world where no water is available. The main problem humanity is facing is that the world is becoming hotter. Less precipitation and less water accumulation have the effect of turning arable land into desert. The loss of freshwater resources is often caused by global warming, overutilization, and contamination.

- Most of the countries in the northern hemisphere do not have a water shortage yet, although that is starting to change. Many countries and, in many cases, entire continents do not have physical access to freshwater either because they simply cannot afford it or because even if they could there's no water to be found.

Ice cubes float to the top of a glass of water because the density of ice is lower than the density of water.

- In addition to drinking, water is also used for sanitation. Without water for sanitation, deadly diseases quickly spread, leading to losses in biodiversity, further accelerating the degradation of arable land and, therefore, the disappearance of any form of life.

- Water scarcity is a highly global issue that affects everybody in one way or another. In the globalized world we live in today, water scarcity will become a serious national security issue, and it's not going to originate only in developing countries. Even in the United States there are a number of states with a critical lack of freshwater.

- Global climate change is changing the situation by making it significantly worse than it's ever been. The main issue is that land is changing from farming land to desert—also known as **desertification**—in which there is much less precipitation and, therefore, less available water both above ground and underground.

- In the case of limited availability of water, one major factor is in the overexploitation of water for hydroelectric energy production. This has become a growing issue in many countries.

Water Contamination
- In addition to having less water, a lot of the water that we do have is contaminated. Contamination due to agricultural practices involves water for irrigation that becomes heavily polluted with pesticides and fertilizers before being disposed into the groundwater, which is responsible for feeding rivers and other freshwater reservoirs.

- There is also contamination from mining. Water has been and still is the main component for both extraction of minerals and natural gas.

- Sometimes we associate the color (and taste) of water to its drinkability, but that can be highly misleading. Brownish water may contain just some sand or soil residue that in small quantities can be okay for drinking.

- Sometimes water that appears crystal clear has within it particles we don't see that can have hazardous effects, such as certain kinds of bacteria or viruses that are invisible to the naked eye.

- Bacteria in water could come from, for example, lack of proper sanitation. If sewages are not controlled, or at least well separated from sources of freshwater, then contamination will likely occur.

- Usually, this type of contamination is controlled chemically by adding chlorine through large and expensive water plants. However, while chlorine can remove dangerous bacteria and viruses, it cannot do anything against some other contaminants, such as heavy metals.

- Sometimes we don't accumulate heavy metals in our body only through the water we drink, but rather through the food we eat. Water contamination, in other words, does not only affect us directly, but also indirectly.

- Contamination from pesticides and, in particular, organophosphates from agriculture is also extremely dangerous. The EPA banned most residential uses of organophosphates in 2001, but they are still sprayed on fruits and vegetables and are used to control pests in public spaces and parks.

- Many of the causes of water contamination are the result of human activity, including groundwater poisoning from the use of fertilization and pesticides, global climate change as a consequence of burning fossil fuels, exploitation of precious metals for industry, exploitation of natural gas reserves, and the attempt to find additional energy sources.

Decontaminating Water

- **Antimicrobial activity**—that is, destroying dangerous bacteria or viruses—is usually carried out by adding chemicals to freshwater. In some cases, chlorine is sufficient, but for many bacteria, chlorine is not enough.

- In principle, we could use antibiotics to kill unwanted bacteria and to cure the water, but any chemical that we add can only attack a particular type of bacteria, making their use rather limited. Such chemicals would then remain in the water, having potential side effects in our bodies and in the environment.

- A better strategy is to design antimicrobial materials. This strategy is more effective than just filtering or killing a particular kind of bacteria. The ultimate advantage is that while bacteria can evolve and adapt to become resistant to antibiotics, that does not happen with antimicrobial materials.

- Nanotechnology has been useful in the design of such materials. For example, silver nanoparticles can attach to the membrane of a cell of a bacterium, completely destroying it. While the use of silver nanoparticles is not yet widespread, we will see a surge in their use in the near future.

- The current solution for the removal of heavy metals is through complex ion exchangers, which are basically filters. Such filters exchange positive metal ions dissolved in solution with harmless chemicals (usually potassium).

© iStockphoto/Thinkstock.

The current solution for the removal of heavy metals from water is through complex ion exchangers, which are basically filters.

- While these systems work pretty well, they have a major limitation: They require a water-intensive regeneration. However, once the "good" ions have all been released, the exchange mechanism stops, and the "bad" ions pass unfiltered.

- Regeneration requires a reverse process, where the collected, bad stuff is replaced with the good stuff. To make that happen, a lot of water is needed. A large-scale regenerating system is expensive because of this.

- In principle, one could design single-use filters. Unfortunately, that would be a costly and impractical solution on a large scale with an additional side effect of a huge amount of waste produced.

- While ion-exchange systems work, a simpler and, most importantly, cheaper system is needed. Instead of an inorganic solution to the problem, in the future we may turn to biology.

- Genetically modified algae can be used for sequestration and disposal of heavy metals. Preliminary results in research labs indicate that not only can algae assimilate these metals, but that they are actually able to reproduce in the presence of these metals, reinforcing an environment favorable for the algae.

- Going nano for some materials may provide a new step forward in water decontamination. The idea is both to stop particles via the filter as well as to maximize the exposure of the water to the antimicrobial surface. This means maximizing the surface-to-volume ratio of the material.

- There is no one material that will be able to do all water decontamination, so scientists are working on combining a diversified and highly specialized set of nanomaterials in order to clean the dirtiest of water by scaling down complex heterogeneous materials while improving the filtering capabilities.

- One idea being pursued is to combine these very small materials with electrophoresis, which drives the fluid and photocatalytic materials, which use power from the Sun to activate the energy-intensive processes required for water decontamination.

- Nanoparticles will also be used for removing metals and organic molecules, including pesticides. Nanotechnology will provide a toolbox at our disposal that can be used and tailored for any specific level of water decontamination.

Desalinizing Water
- New science and technologies could also be used to produce new freshwater. Along this line, saltwater desalination has huge potential. However, optimizing the existing freshwater resources through conservation is also crucial.

- Because of all of the reasons that lead to water contamination and/or scarcity, we need to filter and make new freshwater from seawater. This will be especially important for regions that do not have water sources to begin with.

- Water desalinization is already a vital reality in countries placed in the middle of a desert. The problem is water desalination is expensive, especially in the currency of energy.

- The main reason that desalinization is so energetically expensive today lies in the fact that it's largely based either on boiling water or through a process called reverse osmosis.

- The reverse osmosis process relies instead on the reverse direction of a natural process—namely, **osmosis**—which is the process of balancing concentrations across a membrane.

- Reverse osmosis takes place in reverse, but it needs a strong external pressure to be applied. Under these conditions, salt water can be pushed through a semipermeable membrane separating salt ions and freshwater. Such pressures need to be substantial, and therefore, it's costly.

- One of the greatest and most important challenges to science in this century will be to find new and much cheaper ways to desalinate water. It's going to become a matter of life and death.

- One idea is to use hollow nanofibers, such as carbon nanotubes, as the mechanical filters. The diameter of these tubes is so small that only water can go through because salt doesn't fit. Getting enough flow through the filter is challenging, but scientists are working on ways to improve this aspect.

- In the future, we may think up completely different approaches to making our water. For example, there's a type of beetle in the Namib Desert that has developed the ability to harvest water from fog, and scientists have been trying to mimic this ability on a human scale.

Important Terms

antimicrobial activity: The act of destroying dangerous bacteria or viruses.

desertification: The process by which land on Earth is changing from farming land to desert, in which there is much less precipitation and, therefore, less available water both above ground and underground.

osmosis: The process of balancing concentrations across a membrane.

Suggested Reading

Milazzo, *Unlikely Environmentalists*.

Savage, Diallo, Duncan, Street, and Sustich, *Nanotechnology Applications for Clean Water*.

Vigil, *Clean Water*.

1. How much freshwater do we have on this planet, and where does it come from?

2. What is threatening our freshwater resource, and how will technology help?

Biofuels—The Fuel of the Future?
Lecture 17

W hen we talk about energy needs—to run our cars, to heat our houses, to generate electricity—we usually mean a specific technology, and in particular, we refer to a specific type of fuel. Oil, gas, and coal are fossil fuels that derive from the chemical processing of biological materials (basically plants and animals) over several geologic eras. Fossil fuels are biological in origin; it just takes nature millions of years to convert them into fuel. Biofuels have the same origin as fossil fuels, but the way we obtain biofuels couldn't be more different.

Fossil Fuels versus Biofuels

- Fossil fuels and biofuels have essentially the same biological origin: They generally both belong to the carbon cycle, which involves the release of carbon into the atmosphere—for example, through burning fossil fuels or just the natural breathing of animals and plants—to the absorption and storage of carbon on the ground in the form of vegetation and soil.

- Essentially every living organism is made out of carbon (among other things, of course), and this carbon is conserved in the carbon cycle. Living organisms supply themselves with new carbon through photosynthesis—for plants, by taking in carbon dioxide and using sunlight or by eating as animals do. Once they die, these organisms become part of the food supply for the next generation.

- In the process of decomposing, some of the carbon goes through chemical reactions to become hydrocarbons over a very long period of time. This is the basis for fossil fuels. After millions of carbon cycles, those bits of hydrocarbons accumulated into the massive oil wells we now consume.

- Basically, our current process of utilization of fossil fuel relies on burning it. When we burn it, we transform the carbon in it into carbon dioxide. The problem is that the current process lacks a way to cyclically reconvert that carbon dioxide into fuel again—once the fuel is burned, it's gone.

- The reason we have fossil fuel is essentially because of the Sun, a very high energy source that allows for the transformation of organic and biological material into the fossil fuel.

- **Fossil fuel** is biological material being compressed, turned, and transformed through time, pressure, and temperature into a highly energetic energy source.

- One of the main reasons cars still run on gasoline is because one gallon of gas is unbeatable in terms of energy stored. That massive energy density combined with cheap cost is why we still use fossil fuels so heavily for most of our energy demands.

- We would be able to keep using fossil fuels forever if they weren't finite. Nature made them over millions of years, but only a very limited supply was made, much of which we've already consumed.

- Biofuels are a renewable alternative to fossil fuels; they are as energetic as fossil fuels. Although biofuels and fossil fuels share the same origin, the process we use to make biofuels is artificial, chemically encouraging nature to speed up by a few million years.

- What nature did with biological material to make coal and oil, that is essentially what we do to turn crops and biomass—which is just a generic term for biological waste—into fuel. Just like the natural process of making fossil fuels, it takes a lot of energy to make biofuels.

- The first step to start making biofuel is to grow crops. The Sun provides the energy for the growth, combined with a significant amount of water. After harvesting, cellulose and other fibers chemically similar to sugars are left to ferment. In this sense, making biofuel is similar to making beer or wine.

- Fermentation is an extremely well-known process that essentially uses yeast to consume sugar and produce alcohol and carbon dioxide as waste products.

- The process of fermentation is at the heart of many wide-ranging applications, and because it has been used and improved upon by many people over many centuries, ethanol has been the king of biofuels. It is also referred to as a first-generation biofuel.

- Ethanol is already used quite extensively as a blending agent with gasoline to increase how efficiently it combusts, cutting down on carbon monoxide and other smog-causing emissions.

- Ethanol used for power generation or transportation requires crops that are rich enough in sugars—like corn, for example. The more sugar there is, the more ethanol is produced. However, there are several issues that diminish the appeal for ethanol from corn as the fuel of the future.

- Once we consider the total energy consumed in the production of ethanol, it's clear that the net energy content value added and delivered to consumers is very small. It's even less sustainable if we consider the amount of raw material needed to produce a gallon of alcohol.

- Even if we decide to go with corn to fuel, there is another important ingredient that is needed—namely, water. With a ratio of 3:1 water to corn, a massive water supply is needed for an ethanol-based economy. In addition, water is a highly precious commodity.

- It is quite clear scientifically that ethanol from corn isn't going to replace fossil fuels anytime soon. In terms of the number of gallons of ethanol you can get per acre of crop, corn is one of the absolute worst.

Other Forms of Biofuels

- **Biodiesel** is similar to ethanol, but it can also come from oils and fat. Most biodiesel is made from soybean oil or recycled cooking oils, but animal fats, other vegetable oils, and other recycled oils can also be used to produce biodiesel.

- Biodiesel can be used as a fuel for vehicles in its pure form, but as with ethanol, it's usually used as a petroleum-diesel additive, which reduces the levels of pollution emitted from diesel-powered vehicles. One advantage of biodiesel is that it comes closer to the energy density of gasoline than ethanol.

- Unfortunately, as in the case of corn, biodiesel production is still extremely energy intensive, and it requires chemicals for its manufacturing that also derive from food crops.

- In addition, as efficient as sugarcane is, or as biodiesel may become, they are still fuels derived from crops that we grow to eat. A future world in which we are pitting land use for fuel against land use for food sounds a bit scary.

- Enormous research programs are under way in the United States and around the world to find and engineer other plants to be used as biofuels—preferably, plants that don't serve as a food source, at least for humans.

- Second-generation biofuels get around this fuel-versus-food dilemma by using biomass from nonfood parts of current crops, such as stems, leaves, and husks that are left behind once the food crop has been harvested.

- In addition, second-generation biofuels may simply use crops that in the first place are not meant to be used as food, such as switchgrass. They may also use the waste coming from industry, such as woodchips or the skins and pulp from fruit pressing.

- One of the great advantages of second-generation biofuels is that nearly any kind of wasted biomass can, in principle, be considered as a fuel source.

- Within this class of second-generation biofuels, it's also possible to directly make gas as opposed to liquid. This is called **biogas**, although it's sometimes called swamp gas, landfill gas, or digester gas. Biogas is made of anywhere from 50–80% methane, and the rest is mostly carbon dioxide.

Second-generation biofuels use biomass from nonfood parts of crops that are left behind once the crop has been harvested.

- Natural gas, which is the gas we use in most of our homes, comes from oil wells and is made of about 70% methane, and the rest is other hydrocarbons such as propane and butane.

- When biogas is purified, it can be used as a replacement for natural gas. Biogas is actually the natural by-product of fermentation and decomposition. Any anaerobic decomposition process—that is, where there is no oxygen—naturally releases methane.

- The challenge with many of these second-generation biofuel processes is that it can be more difficult to extract useful feedstock—the stuff we need in order to directly make the fuels—out of the starting biomass.

- Many second-generation biofuels have their useful sugars chemically locked in, which adds to the complexity and, very importantly, to the cost of second-generation biofuels. Still, given all of the research and advances being made, the future of second-generation biofuels holds promise.

The Third Generation of Biofuels

- It would be very interesting if we could directly reconvert carbon monoxide and dioxide into fuel. A living organism whose food source was carbon monoxide and carbon dioxide and whose waste product was fuel might be an enormously important technology of the future.

- Using microorganisms to carry out the energy conversion processes required to turn raw materials into fuel is essentially how the third generation of biofuels works.

- Among these microorganisms, algae have the ability to perform just such a conversion and, therefore, have the potential to be the world's future fuel maker. Basically, algae are fed to get them to produce complex sugars and fats. They are then squeezed to extract these sugars for further processing into biofuel.

- Algae are appealing because they consume carbon dioxide very efficiently, and the fact that they grow in water means that algae could be ideal candidates for recycling carbon from emission sources like power plants or industrial facilities.

- In addition, algae don't need freshwater; they can grow in marine environments or even in dirty wastewater. The fuel they produce also doesn't require any pretreatment before processing, which is necessary for many second-generation biofuels.

- Because of these appealing aspects, a huge scientific effort is currently under way to optimize the energy output of algae so that more fuel can be extracted from the same amount of algae. It will require massive genetic engineering to customize the ability of algae to make more fuel.

- In the emerging field of algae genomics, scientists are trying to modify the algae with genes that could cause the cells to expel the fuel right when they manufacture it, instead of going through the squeezing process.

- Additionally, algae are being genetically engineered to create higher oil or starch content. In this case, we are trying to optimize a completely new process that is able to extract more energy from the input material.

The Future of Biofuels

- Biofuels, even if sustainable and renewable, are still meant to be burned, causing a continuous increase in carbon emissions into the atmosphere. The warmer planet that results would have less water and less fertile land, which means less space for food and also for growing our fuel.

- One future direction for biofuels will be to make them sustainable and to reduce our impact on climate change. Any new fuel that scientists design in the future will most likely be activated or produced using the energy of the Sun, which is the cheapest energy possible.

- Another possibility is to do something akin to artificial photosynthesis. Using carbon dioxide and hydrogen, we could possibly take the Sun's energy to make complex sugars or molecules to be used for energy generation, using synthetic materials as opposed to plants.

- Many of these possibilities are already well understood and demonstrated but will require innovations in science and technology to decrease costs and increase efficiencies and durability.

- The future of biofuels is definitely bright, but the key in finding the best fuels, for whatever particular process that might be needed, is to mimic nature in capturing and harvesting the energy of the Sun in the most efficient way.

biodiesel: A liquid similar to ethanol that is made from soybean oil or recycled cooking oils, but animal fats, other vegetable oils, and other recycled oils can also be used.

biogas: Sometimes called swamp gas, landfill gas, or digester gas, it is made of 50–80% methane, and the rest is mostly carbon dioxide.

fossil fuel: A highly energetic energy source that results from biological material being compressed, turned, and transformed through time, pressure, and temperature.

Suggested Reading

Edwards, *Green Algae Strategy*.

Pahl, *Biodiesel*.

Rosillo-Calle and Johnson, *Food versus Fuel*.

Soetaert and Vandamme, *Biofuels*.

Questions to Consider

1. Is gasoline a biofuel? How do biofuels work? Can the world really grow its fuel?

2. What's the advantage of using algae over corn to make fuel?

Solar Cells—Electricity from the Sun
Lecture 18

S olar cells, or solar photovoltaics, are materials—usually in the form of flat panels—that can convert renewable sunlight directly into electricity. Nearly all types of solar cells are improving in their efficiency over time, but we're still not close to being cost effective with other technologies, renewable or not. Nevertheless, this is an exciting time for solar photovoltaics: Given how quickly we've progressed in just the last 10 years in reducing costs; increasing efficiencies; and designing new, improved materials, the future of solar cells is indeed very bright.

The Power of the Sun

- Despite its tremendous amount of available energy, using the Sun to make electricity is one of the least-utilized renewable resources thus far. In fact, renewable resources overall account for very little of our energy production.

- One of the advantages of solar photovoltaics, or solar cells, over other renewable resources, such as wind or hydropower, is that it is a technology that spans across any size and dimension.

- We not only use a whole lot more power than we used to, but we will be continuing to use more and more—and at an extremely rapid growth rate. Hopefully, we will learn how to use energy more efficiently and perhaps reduce our hunger for energy.

- If we want to curb our carbon dioxide emissions, then about half of that power should come from renewable resources; otherwise, carbon dioxide emissions will continue to rise throughout the century. In that case, resorting to our enormous resource of energy—the Sun—is appealing.

- All renewable technologies have been declining in price over time, but solar photovoltaics are way behind, costing around 5 times as much per watt of power produced compared to the others.

Solar Cells

- A **solar cell** is a material that takes light and converts it to electricity. The light can be thought of as tiny bursts of energy, which are called **photons**. When a photon strikes the material, the energy from it is taken in by a negative charge in the material—an electron—that is then in an excited state because it gains energy from the photon.

- Once the electron is in an excited state, if the material is designed correctly, it can be taken out of the material on one side. When the electron is excited in this way, it also leaves behind a positive charge—a hole—which will exit the material from the other side.

- The energy from the photons gets transferred into negative and positive charges that leave on opposite sides, creating a current. We can then use this current as a power source.

- This special material is known as a **semiconductor**, which doesn't conduct electricity unless there are excited electrons present.

- Often, we represent the states of electrons with simple lines called a band picture. The bottom line refers to the energy level of where electrons are sitting without being excited—the valence band. The top line is where the electron would be in energy if it gets excited by a photon—the conduction band. The difference in energy between the conduction and valence bands is known as the band gap.

- Certain semiconductors, which have valence and conduction bands spaced the right amount apart in energy—that is, with the right band gap—can convert a good amount of sunlight into excited electrons, but we still need a way to get the electrons to move to one side and the holes to move to the other.

- Because an electrically charged particle will feel a force when it is in an electric field, we can put such a field directly inside the material itself by simply adding the right impurities to each side of the material, creating a gradient of electron concentration in the material that generates an internal electric field. The electrons and holes that get excited by the Sun will then immediately feel this field and start to migrate over to their respective ends.

- This kind of material is known as a p-n junction because we call the electron-rich side n-type and the electron-deficient side p-type. If we don't shine light on the material, then what we have is a device called a diode, a material where current only flows in one direction because of its internal electric field.

- The anode and cathode of a circuit represent the negative and positive terminals that can be hooked up to a device to power it. After turning on a light, if we were to connect a wire from the anode to the cathode in a circuit, then we are short-circuiting the solar cell, and there would be no current in the diode. In this case, the current that flows through the rest of the circuit is called the short-circuit current.

- If, on the other hand, we don't connect the anode and cathode but rather just keep the solar cell unplugged—not connected to anything it might power—then all the photocurrent must pass through the diode. This is called the open-circuit voltage; it's how much the voltage drops across the diode when light shines on the material and it is not connected to anything.

- The short-circuit current and the open-circuit voltage are of paramount importance in assessing the efficiency of the solar cell. In fact, it is simply the combination of these 2 measurements that dictate to a large degree how efficient the solar cell will be at converting sunlight into electricity.

- The efficiency of solar cells is steadily increasing over time, but unfortunately, the costs have not come down enough to be competitive with other renewable resources and certainly not with fossil fuels.

- More than 80% of all solar cells today are made out of crystalline silicon, but there are many other materials that can convert sunlight into electricity. Solar cells can also be based on organic polymers or on multiple layers of materials, for example.

- The multilayer solar cells are the most efficient solar cells today, but they're also by far the most expensive, so their application is limited. The ones based on organic materials are the cheapest, but they're also the least efficient, making them not cheaper overall.

The Efficiency of Solar Cells
- The efficiency is the amount of energy that the solar cell makes in the form of electricity divided by the amount of energy it receives from the Sun. Today's solar cells, while much better than a generation ago, still don't convert all that much of the available energy.

- What happens is the sunlight excites the electron with different amounts of energy. Photons from the Sun can have a wide range of energies, and only photons with energy larger than the band gap will get those electrons up above the conduction band so they can be extracted and put to work.

- Therefore, if the electron gets excited way above the conduction band, then it has to find its way back down in energy back to the conduction band before it can be extracted—so it gives off heat, which is lost energy.

- For photons at exactly the band gap, the solar cell is perfect. For photons above the gap, any excess energy they have is wasted. Photons below the gap don't get absorbed. That's why a balance must be struck, and materials with the right gap that strike this balance are optimal ones for solar cells. This is also why solar cells aren't very efficient, and why there's such a low limit to even the theoretically obtainable efficiency.

- The amount of energy that is in sunlight depends on the color of the light itself. Light is a wave, so it has a wavelength associated with it, which is also what determines the color of the light. It also happens to be related to the energy of the photons.

- For very small wavelength light—say, less than 250 nanometers—there's almost no energy from the Sun. At about the UV range, we start to see intensity, which peaks in the visible. There's a whole lot more available energy from the Sun than just in the visible, such as in the infrared region.

Materials and Solar Cells

- Silicon is by far the dominant material in solar cells today. Silicon has close to the optimal band gap, but near the band gap it's pretty inefficient at absorbing photons. It's much better at absorbing UV-wavelength photons than, say, ones in the visible.

Today's solar cells that are placed on rooftops still don't convert much of the available energy from the Sun.

- We can still get silicon to absorb light in that part of the spectrum, but the way we do it is to make it thick—hundreds of microns thick—because it absorbs light poorly. Because it is thick, it needs to be pure, which costs more money.

- Silicon solar cells are expensive because the cost of installing the cells is high. The problem is that even when these solar cells are thin, they're heavy, and installing rigid, heavy things on top of buildings is expensive.

- Another class of solar materials is known as thin-film solar cells, which can absorb light much more efficiently than silicon and, therefore, can be made much thinner—just a micron thick.

- Among the materials that can be made into thin-film solar cells are cadmium telluride, amorphous silicon, and a blend of copper, indium, gallium, and selenium. The advantage in these is that less material is needed, and in some cases, they can be made flexible. In all of these materials, however, the efficiency of the solar cell is lower than that of crystalline silicon cells.

- Plastics, organic polymers that are blended together, are another class of materials that can be made to make electricity from light. Most plastics do not conduct electricity very well—and, therefore, would not make good solar cells—but there are some polymers that can conduct electricity fairly well.

- Many polymers can absorb light very efficiently. In fact, polymers can absorb light so efficiently that we can make solar cells out of them that only need to be 1/10 of a micron thick. The great advantage of using plastics is that they are extremely cheap, and we know how to make them in massive quantities already.

- Many kinds of plastics are very cheap, nontoxic, and can be made at much lower temperatures. In addition, because these materials can be made into a liquid, they can be printed onto the substrate by machines that are similar to an inkjet printer.

- Another kind of material that can make solar cells is conceptually more similar to plants than other examples. These are known as dye-sensitized solar cells, and they are nanoparticles made out of titanium dioxide. Dye-sensitized solar cells are very easy and cheap to make.

- These are only some examples of the wide variety of materials that can be used to make solar cells. In addition to these, many others are being explored today by scientists across the world. These materials are quite different from one another, and they all have their strengths and weaknesses.

- For example, silicon absorbs light poorly. Thin-film materials are not yet as efficient as silicon, and they can suffer from greater variability in their quality control. Some use toxic chemicals such as cadmium, and others use elements that are not abundant such as indium.

- For the organic or plastic solar cells, the challenge is that they are much less efficient—so low, in fact, that they cannot even be used for rooftop installation. For the dye-sensitized cells, the additional packaging required is associated with a high cost.

- Solar cells are rapidly improving, and the possibilities for new materials give enormous hope for the future. The dream of limitless electricity from the Sun is a dream that will revolutionize our world.

Important Terms

photon: A tiny burst of energy that composes light.

semiconductor: A type of special material that does not conduct electricity unless excited electrons are present.

solar cell: A material that takes light and converts it to electricity.

Suggested Reading

Chiras, *Power from the Sun*.

Green, *Third Generation Photovoltaics*.

Komp, *Practical Photovoltaics*.

Lynn, *Electricity from Sunlight*.

Questions to Consider

1. How does a solar cell work? What is the basic set of processes that transforms a photon of light into an electron of current?

2. What has to happen for the world to be able to take advantage of the most abundant renewable energy resource—light?

Batteries—Storing Energy Chemically
Lecture 19

D iscussions about energy are often divided into the supply side, which is how we make the energy, and the demand side, which is how we use it. Most supply today comes from coal, gas, and oil while most of our use is in transportation and buildings; amazingly, half of the energy we supply is wasted as heat. Implicit in such discussions is the idea of storing all of this energy. Today, an increasing amount of our lives is electrified, so temporary storage of electrical energy is becoming much more important. The future currency of energy undoubtedly lies in batteries.

Storing Electrical Energy

- There are many different approaches that can be used to store electrical energy, but the advantage of batteries is that they offer a direct release of stored energy as electricity.

- Fuel sources such as gasoline or mechanical energy still need to be converted into electricity, introducing losses in efficiency as well as a challenge in scaling either down or up in magnitude. Batteries, on the other hand, store energy in the form of chemical reactions, which release electrical current in a straightforward manner.

- The key factors in making a good battery—or, for that matter, any energy-storage technology—is in the density of energy stored both by weight and by volume, in how quickly the energy can be released and recharged and under what conditions, in how safe the technology is, and in the cost and abundance of the materials used.

- Progress has been very slow with volumetric energy density. The energy-storage density of batteries has certainly increased with time, but the current and future needs for reliance on dramatically increased electrical storage calls for a much faster pace of progress.

- If we are ever going to replace fossil-fuel supply-side energy resources with renewable resources on any sort of large scale, then energy storage will be one of the biggest hurdles to overcome.

- Even if wind or solar energy were completely free, we wouldn't be able to use it for more than about 10% of our total electricity needs, simply due to the fact that the technology to store that much energy is not there yet.

Units of Energy

- The main unit of power is the **watt**, which is a rate of energy use that is measured in joules per second. To turn that into a unit of energy, we need to multiply by time. A watt-hour is the amount of energy that gives a watt of power for an hour continuously.

- For batteries, we also commonly use the current at a given voltage as a way to measure how much energy can be stored. **Power**, which is energy per time measured in watts, is also equal to voltage times current.

- **Current** is measured in **amperes**, or amps, and 1 amp is equal to the current that flows when a potential difference of 1 **volt** is placed across a wire with a resistance of 1 ohm. It's a measure of electrical charge passing through a circuit that is equal to more than 10^{18} electrons flowing per second.

- One amp at 120 volts is the same amount of wattage as 10 amps delivered at 12 volts. To convert a battery's amp-hour capacity to watt-hours, simply multiply the amp-hours by the voltage.

The Science of Batteries

- A battery is also known as electrochemical energy storage because it is electricity stored chemically; a battery converts chemical energy from a reaction directly into electrical energy.

- There are 2 different sides to a battery: a side with some chemical A and another side with another chemical C, for example. A (which stands for anode) and C (which stands for cathode) want to react, but they are separated by another material known as an electrolyte, which only allows positively charged components of one of the materials (A) to pass through it.

- Chemical reactions in the battery cause a buildup of electrons at the anode. This results in an electrical difference between the anode and the cathode, which is unstable because of the buildup of the electrons on one side. The electrons don't like such a situation; they want to rearrange themselves to eliminate this difference.

- Electrons repel one another and try to go to a place with fewer electrons. In a battery, the only place to go for those frustrated electrons is to the cathode. However, the electrolyte keeps the electrons from going straight from the anode to the cathode within the battery.

- If there were no electrolyte, the electrons would all go through from A to C, shorting the whole thing and leading to no net current. Instead, when the circuit is closed by connecting a wire from the cathode to the anode, the electrons will be able to respond to the pressure they feel and get over to the cathode. The electrons go through the wire, lighting the lightbulb or powering the electric car along the way.

- At a certain point, once most of those charged bits of material A have made their way across the electrolyte to C, the electrochemical processes change the chemicals in the anode and cathode enough to make them stop supplying electrons. Therefore, there is a limited amount of power available in a battery.

- When you recharge a battery, you change the direction of the flow of electrons using another power source. Then, the electrochemical processes happen in reverse, restoring the anode and cathode to their original state so that they can again provide power. This recharging ability is not possible in all types of battery chemistries.

The History of Batteries

- In 1799, Italian physicist Alessandro Volta created the first battery by stacking alternating layers of zinc, blotting paper soaked in salt water, and silver. This arrangement, now called a voltaic pile, was the first to emit a steady, lasting current.

- In Volta's battery, the electrolyte is the saltwater, which reacts differently with the zinc than with the silver, so a net charge imbalance is created, causing the piled-up electrons to flow through a wire. This simple electrochemistry can be made to occur with different metals.

- It's not easy to scale this battery to large sizes, and there's no easy way to recharge the ions. Therefore, over the past 200 years, many different designs and battery chemistries have been developed, tested, and optimized.

The electromotive unit of force is called a volt in honor of Alessandro Volta (1745–1827), who invented the electric battery.

- First used in 1859, the lead-acid battery is typically used to start a gasoline-powered car. The electrodes are usually made of lead dioxide and metallic lead while the electrolyte is a sulfuric acid solution.

- Lead-acid is one of the oldest rechargeable battery systems; it's rugged, forgiving if abused, and economical in price, although it does have a fairly low energy per weight and somewhat limited cycle life. Still, lead acid batteries are heavily used today.

- Zinc-carbon batteries were first synthesized in 1867 and are based on chemistry involving zinc and carbon. The anode is made out of zinc; the cathode is manganese dioxide; and the electrolyte is ammonium chloride or zinc chloride. These are the kinds of batteries commonly found in many inexpensive AAA, AA, C, and D batteries.

- Another kind of battery chemistry is known as alkaline, which is also common in AA, C, and D batteries. In these, the cathode is made out of a manganese-dioxide mixture while the anode is a zinc powder. This type of battery gets its name from the electrolyte, which is made out of potassium hydroxide, an alkaline material.

- Alkaline batteries have a considerably higher energy density and longer shelf life compared to the zinc-carbon batteries; as a result, alkaline batteries have become immensely popular as the disposable battery of choice. However, they also have a number of disadvantages, including poor recharging ability and a very strong dependence of energy-storage capacity on the load.

- Nickel-cadmium batteries are based on yet another kind of chemistry, and they have been quite popular since the 1950s in portable electronics due to their higher energy density compared to zinc-carbon as well as better recharge capability compared to alkaline batteries.

- Lithium-ion chemistry provides yet another platform for electrochemical energy storage. Lithium is the 3rd lightest element in the periodic table, making it a very appealing material to carry charges without getting too heavy.

- Given the continued decrease in price and the very high energy densities as well as high cycle life, many believe that lithium-ion batteries will be the major rechargeable battery technology for decades to come. Today, there are chemistries based on cobalt, manganese, and phosphate, and each has its own advantages and disadvantages.

The Safety of Batteries

- If overheated or overcharged, lithium-ion batteries can suffer from what is known as thermal runaway and cell rupture, which can lead to combustion in extreme cases.

- If the energy a battery stores is released in a controlled, slow manner, it's perfectly safe, but if it is allowed to all come out at once, it becomes more like a bomb.

- Keeping batteries safe is technologically difficult because a large battery consists of many small batteries packed together, so each single cell needs to have its own individual safety controls and monitoring system.

- Safety features cost extra money and take up valuable space inside the battery pack, which is why enormous amounts of research today are geared toward making lithium-ion batteries as safe as possible. The challenge is to make it safe without losing any of the functionality.

- In the world of batteries, things have certainly improved more rapidly in the last decade than in the previous 20 decades, and lithium-ion batteries seem to be a platform technology for the present and near future.

Batteries of the Future

- In the future, it's going to be very hard to increase energy density much further: Lithium is the most reactive element and the lightest available metal. Lighter cathode materials will likely hold the key to such improvements, but new materials for the new anode may also become important.

- Scientists are exploring how the use of nanostructures could improve stability. New, more stable materials and interfaces will be developed to improve the cycle counts. Someday, batteries will be rechargeable perhaps for millions of cycles.

- Another possible battery of the future is called the lithium-air battery, in which the cathode is completely removed from the battery. These kinds of batteries are still purely in the research stage, but this could become a transformative storage technology.

- In addition to energy density, we'll be seeing a lot of other improvements and changes in our batteries of the future. Completely new ways to make batteries will also be used. We will be able to make batteries out of a wider range of materials that could be cheaper, more abundant, and completely nontoxic.

- There are a few other technologies that are similar to batteries in that they store and give electricity and could compete with batteries in the future. For example, ultracapacitors are based on solid-state devices rather than using layers of wet chemicals.

- Ultracapacitors are giant energy-dense versions of the capacitor, and they can charge and discharge much more quickly than today's batteries. The challenge in ultracapacitors still lies in the energy density, which needs to be considerably larger.

- Fuel cells, on the other hand, are significantly more energy dense than today's batteries. In a **fuel cell**, a fuel source such as hydrogen or hydrocarbons is provided continuously and can be refilled like a gas tank to an electrochemical cell. Fuel cells face major challenges in order to outperform batteries, primarily in cost and lifetime.

- Batteries will likely never compare to gasoline as an energy-storage material—at least not by most measures. Nevertheless, the battery will most certainly be a pivotal energy-storage technology that brings us through the transformation away from a fossil fuel–based energy world.

Important Terms

ampere: The unit of electric current; 1 amp is equal to the current that flows when a potential difference of 1 volt is placed across a wire with a resistance of 1 ohm.

current: The flow of electric charge (measured in amps).

fuel cell: A device that combines 2 chemicals (typically, hydrogen and oxygen), producing electric current in the process.

power: Energy per time measured in watts; equal to voltage times current.

volt: The unit of electric potential in a circuit; a quantitative measure of the electrical potential energy per unit charge.

watt: A rate of energy use that is measured in joules per second; the main unit of power.

Suggested Reading

Aifantis, Hackney, and Kumar, *High Energy Density Lithium Batteries*.

Nazri and Pistoia, *Lithium Batteries*.

Schlesinger, *The Battery*.

Questions to Consider

1. A battery stores electricity chemically. How does it do that?

2. Batteries will likely never be as energy dense as gasoline, so why is there a movement to use them in transportation?

The Hydrogen Economy—Fact or Fiction?
Lecture 20

The promise of a hydrogen economy is one that cannot be realized with current technologies because of the cost of making hydrogen in the first place and of our inability to store this lightest of all known elements in a dense, safe, and economical manner. Today, the dream of a planet that runs on hydrogen is very much alive, but the use of hydrogen as the world's energy currency faces many hurdles that need to be overcome. Scientists are racing toward the future by searching for new materials to make, store, and release hydrogen.

Hydrogen as Fuel

- Hydrogen is the simplest and single most abundant element in the universe, accounting for at least 74% of all the elements. Hydrogen is also the most abundant element in our solar system, and there is a plentiful amount of it on Earth.

- Hydrogen is an abundant domestic resource for just about every nation in the world. For all practical purposes, it's free and the supply is endless—with no potential for generating conflict among people.

- In addition, using hydrogen as fuel has the possibility to be completely clean. When we use the fuel, the product is simply water; there are no other emissions involved.

- Another advantage of hydrogen fuel is that when we need to use it, we can produce directly and efficiently either electricity or heat. Internal combustion engines can essentially be used as is, with little modification, but made to use hydrogen to generate heat instead of fossil fuels.

- A fuel cell can combine hydrogen with oxygen to generate electricity directly. Current fuel cells do so with an efficiency of more than 60%, although improved designs could be more than 80% efficient. On the other hand, out of all the highly dense energy stored in gasoline, the car engine is only able to convert 15%–25% of it into useful mechanical energy.

- Hydrogen fuel is diverse in terms of how it can be generated. It is a fuel that can be made from a variety of different fossil fuels or by splitting water molecules apart using energy provided by renewable resources such as solar or wind. It can also be refueled almost as quickly as gasoline.

Obtaining Hydrogen from Water

- The key difference between a fuel cell and a battery is that the battery has all of its chemicals stored inside, which means that once it converts all of its chemicals into electricity, the battery is either dead or needs to be recharged. With a fuel cell, chemicals constantly flow into the cell, so it doesn't run out like a battery.

- Because hydrogen has such a diverse range of applications on the use side, many believe that this element, comprised of just one proton and one electron, will ultimately be what powers everything.

- Despite the advantages of hydrogen, it powers almost nothing in today's world. Hydrogen is not a source of energy; it is only a way of storing and transporting it. Therefore, hydrogen should not be compared directly with coal and oil or with the Sun and wind.

- Furthermore, there is virtually no hydrogen gas left on Earth, so hydrogen fuel has to be manufactured by extracting it from water or from other hydrogen-containing resources like methane. Therefore, it takes energy to make hydrogen—lots of energy, in fact. This is one of the reasons that hydrogen is not yet powering the world.

- More than 90% of today's hydrogen is produced from fossil fuel sources. In a process called steam reforming, the fossil fuel is mostly converted into hydrogen and carbon dioxide. With this approach for making hydrogen, we are relying heavily on fossil fuels and contributing to global warming.

- We can also make hydrogen from water, but drinking water is extremely precious, so we wouldn't want to be making our world's fuel with it.

- The nondrinkable seawater that covers 2/3 of the planet is an ideal source for hydrogen. In fact, it's much better than freshwater for producing hydrogen because the salt makes it more electrically conductive.

- The simplest way to get hydrogen from water is to just heat it up until the hydrogen breaks apart from the oxygen. Unfortunately, that temperature is 2700°C—far too hot to be practical or economical. Instead, we can encourage the hydrogen and oxygen in water molecules to split apart using an electric current in a process known as **electrolysis**.

Cryogenically cooled liquid hydrogen is the fuel of choice for U.S. space shuttles.

- Through the process of electrolysis, a closed circuit is created involving electrons in the wire and hydroxide ions in the water. The energy delivered by the electricity source is stored by the production of hydrogen.

- The process of electrolysis might be the way our world makes the majority of its fuel in the future. It's simple, and when the source of electricity comes from a renewable source of energy like the Sun, it has completely zero emission during operation.

- Today, only 4% of the total hydrogen produced comes from electrolysis of water because of cost. It costs between 3 and 10 times more to make hydrogen from water than making hydrogen from fossil fuels, so it simply cannot yet compete economically.

- Part of the key to reducing the cost of turning seawater into fuel lies in the use of an appropriate catalyst, which is an electrode material that encourages the reaction to happen more efficiently. By itself, the reaction produced through electrolysis is far too slow to be practical on large scales.

- The problem is that for water splitting, it's been challenging to find really good catalysts, ones that make the reaction happen efficiently and that are also based on cheap and abundant materials.

- So far, the ideal catalyst has not been developed, but many promising recent discoveries point toward a future in which such materials will be available. In fact, some materials known as **photocatalysts** combine the 2 functions of generating electricity from sunlight and acting as an efficient catalyst to split water into the same material.

- When the process of splitting water is made easier and cheaper and based on sunlight, then the dream of imitating the process of photosynthesis could be realized, but that still would be solving only the problem of generating hydrogen cheaply. We still are left with the problem of storing it.

- The key issue is that hydrogen, in its natural state, is a gas, and gases are not very dense. The low volumetric density of gaseous fuels requires a storage method that makes the fuel denser.

- Just as we can make water into a liquid, why not simply use hydrogen as a liquid? Like water, hydrogen exists in all 3 phases but at much different temperatures and pressures.

- To make hydrogen into a liquid, you need to apply a pressure as well as cool the gas down to $-423°F$. In addition to the energy needed to make the hydrogen so cold, liquid hydrogen requires specialized tanks, which have to be highly insulated. This adds costs as well as additional weight for the tank. Liquid hydrogen also has less energy density by volume than gasoline by about a factor of 4.

Alternatives to Liquid Hydrogen
- Scientists and engineers are working on keeping the hydrogen as a gas but compressing the gas down so that it's under very high pressure. The advantage of compressed hydrogen is that it takes a lot less energy to make. You also wouldn't need the tank to have all of that specialized insulation.

- The disadvantage of compressed hydrogen is that the tank needs to be able to hold those large pressures in a very safe way. Also, hydrogen gas has good energy density by weight but poor energy density by volume compared to gasoline or liquid hydrogen, which means it needs a larger tank to store the same amount of energy.

- For different energy-storage technologies, it's tough to beat gasoline in terms of both the energy stored by weight and the energy stored by volume combined. Hydrogen actually stores more energy by weight, but it's the volume that poses the most challenge.

- Some are pushing for the first hydrogen cars to use gasoline as their fuel but to make hydrogen on board out of that gasoline and then either couple it to a fuel cell to make electricity for an electric car or burn the hydrogen directly and use it in a combustion engine.

- The advantage in that scenario is that it would start to get hydrogen-powered vehicles out on the roads while holding on to the large energy densities we're used to with gasoline. The disadvantage is that by using gasoline, it would not be much of an improvement for the environment or for our dependence on oil.

Physically versus Chemically Storing Hydrogen

- Both compressed gas and liquefied hydrogen are what are known as physical storage techniques because they are based on physically confining the hydrogen molecules, albeit in quite different temperature or pressure operating regimes.

- Physical storage techniques are the technologies that are readily available today for storing hydrogen. They may be too expensive, and they may not have ideal energy density, but car manufacturers are already building prototype fleets based on these physical storage technologies.

- Apart from physical storage technologies, scientists are also looking at ways to use chemical storage. In this case, hydrogen is stored either on the surfaces of a solid (called adsorption) or within the solid (by absorption).

- In **adsorption**, hydrogen is attached to the surface of a material either as hydrogen molecules or as hydrogen atoms. In **absorption**, hydrogen is dissociated into hydrogen atoms, and then the hydrogen atoms are incorporated into the atomic framework of the solid.

- One appealing aspect of storing hydrogen chemically in solids is that it makes it possible to store larger quantities of hydrogen in smaller volumes at low pressure and temperatures. It's also possible to achieve volumetric storage densities even greater than liquid hydrogen. This is also the most intrinsically safe of all methods of storing hydrogen.

- As appealing as storing hydrogen chemically seems, there are major challenges that would need to be overcome before it becomes a practical reality. One of the main challenges is that it needs a lot of extra energy, so the benefit of storing more energy is lost.

- For the reversible kind of chemical storage, there is no one material yet that meets all of the desirable attributes.

The Future of Hydrogen

- The hydrogen economy will not result from a straightforward replacement of the present fossil fuel–based economy. Many innovations and technological breakthroughs will be required to address the costs, energy efficiency, and distribution issues.

- The hydrogen fuel for the near future will probably be supplied in the form of pressurized or liquefied molecular hydrogen that is trucked from existing, centralized production facilities, but over time, hydrogen produced in distributed rather than centralized facilities will dominate.

- This kind of hydrogen production will hopefully be done with the advent of new techniques for cheap electrolysis of water by developing new, cheap materials to catalyze the splitting of water. Nanotechnology is likely to play an important role in this discovery.

- Storing the hydrogen efficiently and economically in the future will rely on breakthroughs in materials. The ultimate energy carrier of the future will no doubt be electricity.

- Coupled with renewable sources of energy, the generation and storage of hydrogen provides a very appealing way to transport this currency from one place to another. The future of a global hydrogen economy may still not be all that close, but when oil and natural gas—and even someday coal—are exhausted, the great fuel that powers our world may be based on water.

Important Terms

absorption: The process in which hydrogen is dissociated into hydrogen atoms, and then the hydrogen atoms are incorporated into the atomic framework of the solid.

adsorption: The process in which hydrogen is attached to the surface of a material either as hydrogen molecules or as hydrogen atoms.

electrolysis: A process in which the hydrogen and oxygen in water molecules can be encouraged to split apart using an electric current.

photocatalyst: A material that combines the functions of generating electricity from sunlight and acting as an efficient catalyst to split water into the same material.

Suggested Reading

Gupta, *Hydrogen Fuel*.

Joint Research Centre, *Hydrogen Storage*.

Questions to Consider

1. Name the 2 key technology challenges to enabling a hydrogen economy.

2. Although it is neither, in the context of energy, is hydrogen more like an electron or a photon? Is hydrogen a source of energy or a carrier of energy?

Nuclear Energy—Harnessing Star Power
Lecture 21

N
uclear energy once held up as the answer to all of our energy needs, promising nearly limitless energy with no emissions. Nuclear energy is indeed used widely today—with 20% of U.S. power deriving from nuclear energy—but it has faced major challenges. There are many technological issues that make nuclear fusion still unfeasible, and the timescales to new technologies will likely be long and slow, but the future may allow us to use the enormous built-in power of the atom for nearly limitless, clean energy.

Nuclear Energy Generation

- Most of the ways we produce energy today—for example, by burning oil, coal, or gas—rely on chemical reactions of some sort. The fact that they are explosive means that a lot of energy is freed during the reaction. That energy is captured and further transformed into electrical energy or heat.

- Nuclear power generation is similar to these conventional power-generation systems but with a very important difference: Rather than violently breaking apart chemical bonds between atoms (which causes combustion), nuclear energy is produced by breaking or making individual atoms themselves.

- Nuclei are what make up the core part of atoms, which are then surrounded by electrons, or tiny negatively charges particles. The nucleus is made up of protons and neutrons, which are also referred to as subatomic particles because they are smaller than the atom.

- The mass of the total nucleus is always less than the mass you would get if you added up all the individual protons and neutrons that make it up. Einstein very famously showed this in his equation $E = mc^2$—namely, that mass and energy are equivalent.

- If we can give mass and get energy—and vice versa—then we can understand why the nucleus does not weigh as much as the sum of its parts: excess energy, which is called the nuclear binding energy.

- To tear an electron away from an atom takes a few electron volts of energy—the typical amount of energy stored in a chemical bond—but to break apart a couple of nuclear particles from one another would require 30 million electron volts.

- Different elements on the periodic table are bound by different amounts of energy, which means that the glue that holds those protons and neutrons together is stronger or weaker depending on the element.

- The lighter elements have less nuclear binding energy, which increases as the elements get heavier, and there is a peak around iron. Then, for elements heavier than iron, the binding energy goes down slowly.

Nuclear Fission

- The technology used today for energy generation is called **nuclear fission**. In this process, a neutron comes along and strikes a heavy atom, which then splits into 2 lighter atoms, releasing energy as well as more free neutrons. These neutrons in turn strike another heavy atom, causing it to break apart—and so on.

- The reason fission can produce energy is that the binding energy of the by-product atoms—that is, how much energy is in all that nuclear glue that holds the protons and neutrons together—is larger than that of the starting element. This is why fission happens for heavier elements only.

- The heat produced by nuclear fission reactions is substantially higher than in conventional power plants based on coal or natural gas, and this has significant implications.

- Another important aspect that makes nuclear energy generation different from other sorts of thermal power generation systems is the fact that because a chain reaction occurs, the process can become self-sustaining, and it can also increase violently if not controlled.

- The reaction must be controlled in order for it to be a useful energy technology. This is done by inserting specific materials into the nuclear core that slow down the reaction by absorbing neutrons away from the atom.

- If we can control the nuclear reactions so that they do not run away and become a bomb but, rather, occur at a pace we set, then the result is that the nuclear material simply heats up and, in turn, will heat up whatever we put near it. By being in control, we can harvest nuclear energy in a clean way; nuclear power does not emit any greenhouse gases.

United States Department of Energy.

In 1979, an accident at the Three Mile Island nuclear power plant in Pennsylvania made people wonder whether nuclear power was safe.

- Uranium beats pretty much any other high-energy material in terms of energy per dollar. The amount of energy per kilogram in reactor-grade uranium is close to 100,000 times as much as in the same amount of gasoline. The energy density is so high that very little material is needed.

- The costs of nuclear energy are usually in the actual construction of the power plant, which is about $3 billion; despite this cost, the high energy density makes nuclear power pretty inexpensive to operate.

The History of Nuclear Energy

- When nuclear energy started to be used to generate electricity in the 1950s, it seemed like energy could be created almost by magic. Futuristic scenarios in which a basically infinite source of power was found had everybody greeting these new power generation systems with awe and admiration.

- This optimistic view continued and stimulated the opening of several nuclear power plants during the 1950s and 1960s, but in 1979, an accident at the Three Mile Island nuclear power plant near Harrisburg, PA, had people starting to wonder if nuclear power could be at all safe.

- On April 26, 1986, a reactor in Chernobyl not only failed but went into a complete meltdown. An extremely high level of radiation contaminated the surroundings, and highly toxic chemicals were released into the air and were carried all over Europe. Suddenly, people there felt exposed to an invisible enemy.

- When a massive earthquake hit Japan and an equally massive tsunami struck the nuclear power plant at Fukushima, the world woke up again to face another nuclear dilemma. The tsunami damaged the piping responsible for cooling the reactor and waste storage, and a scenario even scarier than Chernobyl appeared in which the chain reaction would increase substantially.

- The escalating gravity of the situation at Fukushima highlighted another crucial aspect of nuclear power generation: What appeared to be a minor accident became, within a short amount of time, a major one with a core meltdown and major releases from waste that is not cooled.

Issues with Nuclear Power

- Nuclear power is not a renewable source of energy. While uranium is common in Earth's crust, its total supply is finite. In addition, just like for oil, the material is available only in specific parts of the world, which makes it more susceptible to market fluctuations and affects the final cost of electricity generated by nuclear reactions.

- Nuclear energy is not renewable because once the fuel is used up, it cannot be reused or recharged. Instead, the fuel becomes a dangerous material that needs to be disposed of with great care and takes millennia to become safe again.

- There are 2 major issues with nuclear power in terms of cleanliness: the safety and possibility of accidents and the actual exhaust of the nuclear reaction, the nuclear waste.

- We do not yet have the technology to use the by-products of nuclear reactions as fuel for further reactions, so they remain as waste—in some cases, for hundreds of thousands of years. Finding a place to store such waste isn't easy, given the geological time required.

- Because nuclear material can be used for belligerent purposes, there are also geopolitical implications in the use of nuclear power. The risk of uncontrolled uranium enrichment requires a high level of control for how radioactive materials travel from country to country.

Nuclear Fusion

- Rather than large-scale plants, which are immensely costly to build, one direction for the future of nuclear technology is to try to build portable plants. Smaller units could significantly reduce the cost of production, and given the smaller requirements for the core, it could provide a potentially easier way to control the reaction.

- Such reactors may also be able to use nuclear fission to a fuller extent. While current power plants do not extract energy from nuclear waste because the waste can't give off quite enough energy to run the steam turbines efficiently, smaller plants might be able to do so.

- While uranium is the current nuclear fuel, it does have many downsides. Another type of nuclear energy is called **nuclear fusion**, in which small, lightweight atoms are brought together, and when they fuse to form a new type of atom, massive amounts of energy get released in the process.

- We use much simpler and lighter elements—on the other side of the iron peak—for the fusion reaction compared with fission, and very importantly, we are bringing atoms together to form a final material that is harmless: There is no nuclear waste.

- The by-product of fusion is helium, which is inert and in fact useful for a variety of applications. Nuclear fusion is the process that goes on continuously to give the Sun its energy.

- From an energy-density and economic standpoint, nuclear fusion is by far the one with the highest specific energy at 4–5 times as much per kilogram as nuclear fission. The cost of the fuel is balanced by the enormous amount of energy produced; only a very small amount of fuel would be needed.

- The problems with nuclear fusion, and the reasons we do not use it for energy production today, include that it produces too much power to contain and the reaction is simply too hot. We have not figured out a way to slow it down and control it as in the case of fission.

- The only hope we have for utilizing nuclear fusion is if the plasma of fuel within which nuclear fusion takes place could be confined by something that does not use walls or containers.

- In fact, we can contain materials using fields of energy, but that hasn't worked yet in a way that is viable on a large scale, and scientists have been working on it for over 50 years.

- Many scientists have wondered whether fusion could be reached at more manageable temperatures. Claims of having achieved cold fusion have been proposed over the decades and continue to arise periodically, but any real demonstration of cold fusion has yet to exist, and the idea remains much more of a myth than science.

- We have in fact been able to make nuclear fusion reactors, but only in a completely uncontrolled manner. Just as uncontrolled nuclear fission leads to the atomic bomb, uncontrolled nuclear fusion leads to a much more powerful bomb: the hydrogen bomb, or H-bomb.

- Getting nuclear fusion to ignite in the first place represents the second major challenge for nuclear fusion. In fusion reactions, we have to bring together 2 very small atoms that do not want to be near one another. Therefore, to make a hydrogen bomb explode, we have to first light it with an atomic (or fission) bomb.

The Future of Nuclear Power

- Enormous scientific efforts are under way to study both of the major hurdles to utilizing nuclear fusion by, for example, trying to understand and control the fusion ignition process using massive lasers and by building a commercial fusion reactor.

- These programs are massive, multibillion-dollar efforts with facilities larger than football fields and teams of 100s of scientists, but if nuclear fusion can be controlled, this investment will be extremely worthwhile.

- While the future of nuclear energy as we know it today—namely, nuclear fission—is unclear due to the issues of safety, maintenance, upkeep, and waste management, a future based on nuclear fusion would mean the end of our energy dependence on oil.

Important Terms

nuclear fission The splitting of heavy nuclei to release energy.

nuclear fusion: A nuclear reaction in which light nuclei join to produce a heavier nucleus, releasing energy in the process.

Suggested Reading

Ferguson, *Nuclear Energy*.

Mahaffey, *Atomic Awakening*.

Seife, *Sun in a Bottle*.

Questions to Consider

1. Why is there a peak in the nuclear binding curve?

2. Why is nuclear fusion so appealing, and what are the biggest challenges that must be overcome for us to use it?

Prediction—From Storms to Stocks
Lecture 22

As many have observed, it's difficult to make predictions—especially about the future. Science forms the basis of prediction. The process of collecting vast amounts of experimental data and developing theories that can be tested against this data and that can be used to make predictions is ultimately what allows us to see into the future. However, in the future, we may carry with us in our phones a massive life-prediction engine that is constantly changing and updating itself to reflect how healthy we are and how healthy we will be.

The History of Predicting the Future

- Predicting anything about the future presumes an understanding of time. The calendar itself can be considered the simplest kind of predictive device; all human activities run on a strict cycle dictated by a calendar.

- In ancient times, solar and stellar motions in the sky were used to keep track of the passage of time. Complex calendars, similar to the one developed by the Mayans, tracked time with extreme accuracy. Modern-day calendars are not too different in many respects.

- Up until the Middle Ages, high priests, oracles, and magicians were responsible for making predictions about the future by probing the state of mind of the gods and translating them for the common people.

- During the Renaissance, a combination of legends and interpretations of the stars were also used to make predictions, but rather than being prophetic in the sense of being fully supernatural, many prophets of that time tried to combine the evolution of planetary configurations with actual events.

- The power of the scientific method resides in its cyclic testing of assumptions against data. This requires a scientist to make predictions based on the theory that is developed to explain a phenomenon and the observation of the phenomenon itself. These predictions are not based on any supernatural or subjective opinion, but rather on careful observation.

- Sometimes the development of a theory and its realization into an engineered product feeds into more predictions by stimulating and shaping the way we think about the future.

Forecasting the Weather

- Weather forecasting is one of the oldest ways in which science and technology have been used to predict a future phenomenon. Ideally, in forecasting the weather, we'd like to be able to predict the state of the atmosphere above us in any given location and at any given time.

- Forecasting weather is not easy because the state of the atmosphere depends on an incredibly complicated range of factors, many of which are highly interdependent on one another.

- Instead, the most common way to forecast weather today is much simpler—using today's conditions to forecast the conditions of tomorrow based on the enormous approximation that we have a steady atmosphere, which we do not.

- Air pressure is usually associated with the development of good or bad weather. Barometers, which measure the air pressure, have been used for quick weather prediction, but such a measurement is usually not reliable over periods of time longer than a few hours or maybe a day.

- When the pressure is high at the surface of the planet, it means that air is slowly descending. As air descends, it warms, which inhibits the formation of clouds.

- This is why high pressure is generally—but not quite always—associated with good weather. The air that descends in high-pressure areas has to get to high altitudes in some way, and it's done by rising in areas where the pressure is low at the surface.

- As air rises, it cools. As the air cools, the humidity in it begins to condense into tiny drops of water—or, if it's cold enough, into tiny ice crystals. If there's enough water or ice, rain or snow begins to fall. This is why low pressure is associated with bad weather.

- Combining air pressure with visual observations of cloud motion over different locations may be used in what we call today **nowcasting**, which is accurate weather forecasting in a very short range of time. This is, in principle, enough to get a reasonable prediction of the weather.

- The basic idea of numerical weather prediction is to sample the state of the weather, including air, water, and land measurements at a given time and for a specific location. Then, based on the input provided, the models use equations to estimate the state of the biosphere at some time in the future.

- Today, we can use these models to give an acceptable prediction of the weather on the order of days, but when we venture to understand longer times, things become a lot more complicated. Technology has had a huge impact in facilitating the delivery of such forecasts in real time.

- A major part of modern weather forecasting is the severe weather alerts and advisories, which are issued when hazardous weather is expected. Forms of these advisories include severe thunderstorm, tornado, flood, and fog warnings.

- As the computational power available continues to increase, we are able to solve more complex models that take more experimental data as input, and our ability to predict the weather will get much better.

Computers and Predicting

- Since their invention, computers have been used to simulate and predict the weather. In fact, it was not until the 1950s that the computation time needed to solve the models was reduced to less than the forecast period itself. Since then, the evolution in computing has brought forecasting to a completely new level.

- Thanks to such computing power, more complex models can now be solved that combine together atmospheric models with land models, ice models, and ocean models.

- Improvements in prediction are not only about better long-term forecasting, but also about deriving more out of the forecasting we do. In the future, we will see a much deeper connection between the prediction of weather and different aspects of our lives.

National Oceanic and Atmospheric Administration.

ENIAC, one of the earliest massive computing machines, was used to create the first weather forecasts in the 1950s.

- In general, we will use the technology of weather forecasting to be able to see the role of particular events in a bigger picture, which allows us to further refine and develop our models. Ultimately, we seek to understand on very long time scales how both human and natural phenomena impact the environment as a whole.

Predicting Earthquakes

- Prediction of the future doesn't always need to be far ahead; sometimes it can be crucially important if it's only a few hours ahead. When the earthquake hit Japan in 2011, it would have helped enormously to have a way to predict the effects of the earthquake on the production of the tsunami that followed.

- Currently, many different methods for forecasting earthquakes have been suggested. So far, all of these methods look at possible precursors to earthquakes—not causes. Essentially, they all look at early warnings that we humans cannot detect.

- For example, some models look for increased levels of radon, a common underground radioactive gas whose release can be associated with underground changes due to rock cracking. In practice, however, many other factors affect the level of radon fluctuations that can be measured, so this method has failed so far.

- One of the problems in developing better ways to predict earthquakes is due to the fact that we know very little about the conditions and structures of underground faults and of the plates themselves. In order to understand quakes, and therefore to predict them, it is crucial to know more about the dynamics of the soil.

- Technology is providing specialized tools in the form of satellites to accurately measure and provide large amounts of useful data—not only about the dynamics of the soil, but also about their possible effects on other factors, including electromagnetic radiation.

- The deployment of small-scale satellite systems will provide valuable data to develop new methods and models for much more accurate prediction. These models, when combined with weather forecast models, will be able to predict a wide range of other impacts on the environment, including tsunamis, landslides, and many other phenomena.

- In the future, forecasting may need to be interpreted using artificial intelligence, which will be able to collect competing bits of information into a final decision, possibly mediated by some degree of probability.

Prediction and Stock Markets

- Markets are so complex that many think the idea of forecasting their behavior is simply illusory. They believe that any little detail in the market can turn into a new market scenario.

- To dispute this idea, predictive models have been developed, such as **back-propagation algorithms**. In this approach to seeing the future, the model of the stock market is continuously fed with previous performance data, including how wrong the model would have been in the past.

- While widely used today, this system cannot forecast unexpected events that can alter the stock market itself. Furthermore, it always looks at the past rather than at the future to make predictions.

- To remedy this, **genetic algorithms** have been developed. Essentially, instead of looking at the past, models are designed and left to evolve to their most natural state. The genetic component has to do with the idea that the strongest scenario will prevail.

- In the future, these techniques will be complemented with the ability to probe what are called parallel universes through the use of data mining. Essentially, more than one strong solution may prevail, and the evolution of each, independently, will be analyzed. The resulting forecast will be able to give different scenarios with some degree of probability—just like life.

Prediction Markets

- As markets become more predictable, more people will go for the best option. By going for the best option, they will drive the realization of a scenario faster than it would have occurred naturally. Prediction becomes more and more strongly tied to outcome.

- This artificial way to use prediction to alter the outcome—through **prediction markets**—is becoming an extremely novel way to probe and eventually change the course of events.

- The idea of prediction markets is—just as in a real stock market—that the market will decide the real value of a prediction. Just as the value of a company will settle depending on many factors (success in the last quarter, new products, good marketing), the same can hold for predictions in a general sense.

- Prediction markets cannot really be used to predict complex but rationally defined problems such as the weather; rather, their potential is in predicting the outcome of events whose determining factors depend on irrational or subjective factors, such as the stock market and elections.

- In the future, we will use the great potential of prediction markets in the form of a probability for an event to take place as inputs for computing prediction models. The future of prediction and forecasting will see this type of combined approach become commonplace.

- In addition to complex modeling and the use of artificial intelligence, prediction markets extended to a large audience may provide a buffer in limiting bogus attempts aimed not at predicting the future but at changing it, such as polling by the media.

- In place of oracles and magicians, the fortune-tellers of the future will be highly sophisticated machines that will use artificial intelligence and complex modeling of human behavior to predict events. New supercomputers set to the task of predictive medicine can conduct screening tests for predispositions to genetic defects or diseases before we're born.

- The real revolution in predicting our health future is only partially going to lie with genomics. In the future, both genetic and environmental information will be folded into very complex models to estimate our chances, beyond genetics, of our long-term quality of life.

Important Terms

back-propagation algorithm: In this approach to seeing the future, the model of the stock market is continuously fed with previous performance data, including how wrong the model would have been in the past.

genetic algorithm: Essentially, instead of looking at the past, these models are designed and left to evolve to their most natural state. The genetic component has to do with the idea that the strongest scenario will prevail.

nowcasting: Accurate weather forecasting in a very short range of time.

prediction market: An artificial way to use prediction to alter the outcome of an event.

Suggested Reading

Gardner, *Future Babble*.

Hodgson, *Basic Essentials*.

Morlidge and Player, *Future Ready*.

Orrell, *The Future of Everything*.

Questions to Consider

1. How do complexity and accountability factor into making a good prediction?

2. How far are we from predicting human behavior?

Communication—Transcending Time and Space
Lecture 23

We humans are social animals, and we apply our greatest ingenuity to finding ways to connect with one another. The power of encoding a message with a protocol of communication so that it can be distributed is essential for effective and articulated communication. Today, digital communication allows for the transmission of massive sets of digital data of all kinds: images, conversations, videos, calls, chats, radio, and television. Anything that can be digitized can also be transported and made available through the Internet.

Forms of Communication

- The simplest and oldest form of communication is oral—that is, the transmission of a message, idea, or emotion by voice alone. **Oral communication** includes the legends and songs that were passed down to us generation by generation.

- When the communication is recorded, then it falls into a second category: **written communication**. This category includes any form of communication that is written, stamped, or carved on a supporting material.

- Whether oral or written, communication depends on interaction between human beings, which means there is potential for chaos, so the first factor driving the evolution of communication was the need for a set of rules to give us common ground.

- A second driving force was the need to overcome the limitations imposed by the physical boundaries of space and time. New technologies were designed to augment human capabilities for face-to-face communication, making it possible to deliver a message to another time and place.

- Because human interactions in general are a lot more complex than those in other animals, our requirements led to the early development of a critical new technology: language.

- A **language** is a human technology that arises from the needs to provide a common ground for communication. It's an easy way to categorize an abstract concept.

- The major advantage of oral communication is the greatly improved ability to avoid misunderstanding. Once the rules of the language are well defined, a conversation can take place and a lot of good things can happen.

- The technology that enables this most basic form of oral communication is the ability to produce and detect sound waves. For this to happen, 3 things are required: a medium for the sound waves to propagate in; a sound-generation system: our vocal cords; and a sound-detection system.

- Without a medium, we couldn't have sounds or any oral communication whatsoever. Sound comes from the wavelike motion of individual air molecules as a result of a big push given when the sound is created. The information in oral communication is contained in the modulation of propagating waves.

- Air is just one medium, but there are plenty of others that can be used for communication. Water is another one. Beyond air and water, you can listen and therefore communicate through solid media as well.

- In order to communicate orally, humans have developed an incredibly articulated way to generate sound waves. By adjusting the tension in our vocal chords with specifically designed muscles, we can generate waves with different frequencies, which can then be used to modulate sounds to carry information.

- Our hearing, through an equally sophisticated mechanism, transforms this information into electric signals for our brain to process. The sound waves come into contact with the eardrum, generating and amplifying the waves, which propagate through a fluid-filled organ called the cochlea. Inside, very small hairlike sensors pick up the vibration, transforming it into an electrical signal sent to the brain.

- When hearing is severely impeded through damage to the eardrum, the small ear bones, or to those hairlike sensors in the cochlea, major advances in technology allow us to restore much of it.

Advancements of Oral Communication
- Oral communication does have some limitations: Someone needs to be within hearing distance, and they need to understand our language. To supplement these limitations, humans developed an even more groundbreaking technology than language: the alphabet.

- The ability to archive information through a written language allows us to pass knowledge from one generation to the next. In addition, once the language is written down, it becomes possible to translate from one language to another.

- The earliest forms of writing that we know about were carved into stone, which are great in that they last a long time, but they're certainly not very portable. The development of paper from plants was a technological breakthrough that came about for the sole purpose of written communication.

- Writing on paper has been the main form of written communication for more than 2 millennia. Well into the Middle Ages, books were handwritten in a slow and costly process.

- However, technology brought a radical change: With the printing press, what took days or weeks to complete by hand now took only hours, and many copies of the same manuscript could be printed at a very small fraction of the cost.

- One of the major consequences of the printing press was the ability to print fairly cheaply not only important volumes, but also everyday matter. Newspapers were born essentially because of this, but also with the idea that world events are worth reporting, especially now that it was so much easier to do.

- For centuries, written communication moved around the world at a very slow pace, limited by the speed a horse or ship could travel. We needed another medium to enable fast and long-distance communication.

- The most appealing medium is light waves, the speediest known waves in the universe. The speed of light is so much faster than that of sound that it appears to be almost instantaneous in comparison.

- The telegraph brought long-distance, real-time communication to fruition. It used a completely new technology, taking advantage of the newly discovered electromagnetic properties of light: that an electromagnetic pulse made of electrons running at the speed of light through a wire could carry a signal anywhere on the planet.

Roll-to-roll processes such as those used in printing presses can be used to quickly make nanotechnological solar cells.

- The telegraph allowed for an immediate delivery of important messages, but its main limitation was the fact that a message could be delivered only from and to places that had a telegraphic wire. It turns out, however, that the metal wire is not necessary for transmitting electromagnetic waves.

- Electromagnetic waves can propagate in a different medium—air. This has massive implications because it essentially means that we don't need wires to communicate, sparking the beginning of wireless communication.

- As a successor to the wired telegraph, the telephone came next and, with it, the ability to hear over long distances the voice of someone else, which brought new life to oral communication.

- Next came the combination of the 2: telephone and wireless information transfer. The evolution of telephony from fixed to cellular enabled personal communication to occur in any place or at any time.

- Wireless radio communication introduced the new concept of **broadcasting**, which means to transmit for general use. With radio first and television next, communication could take place one way. With television, global communication could also include nonverbal communication because now the viewer could see in real time what was happening.

- Using the same vehicle for transmission of information, a new information revolution began to unfold, and this time it had to do with the way we encode information in electromagnetic waves.

- The technology that enabled wireless radio communication is based on the transmission of an analog signal. What this means is that we encode the information to be sent either by changing the amplitude of the wave or by changing the frequency of the wave.

- The main limitation with wireless radio communication is that it's serial: We can only submit a single piece of information at one time. In addition, interference effects with other radio waves can significantly lower the quality of the signal. Finally, there is only so much information that can be packed into a given carrier wave with analog encoding.

Digital Communication

- The solution that overcomes most of the problems of wireless radio communication is digital communication. Instead of modulating waves in a continuous way, we encode the information into simply 2 states: on or off—a 1 or a 0. The advantage is that much more information can be transported at the same time through the same signal, efficiently and with minimal loss.

- The major breakthrough that was made possible by the development of the transistor was the rise of the Internet and the beginning of what we now call the digital age.

- As a communication platform, just like the radio frequency spectrum was for radio and television, the Internet has had an impact on every possible type of communication. The amount of information that can be exchanged is vastly larger than what was possible via conventional radio channels.

- We can think of the Internet as being like a set of roads, highways, and railways that enable the exchange of information. As with conventional roads, the Internet is similar: It has its own efficiencies and inefficiencies and ways to make the transport of information more efficient whenever possible.

- Two main technological efforts are required for efficiency: the development of high-capacity highways that are capable of carrying a staggering amount of data and the development of high-efficiency vehicles—protocols and formats to carry information efficiently and in the most compact and economical way.

- Current technology efficiently compresses vast amounts of data in such a way that it can be transported online without jamming up the highways. The power of novel compression tools, formats, and protocols enable what once was impossible.

- The Internet is not only about an efficient way of communicating large amounts of information; it's also about enabling entirely new forms of communication. For example, Wikipedia has shown us that the combined knowledge of many users can be as effective, if not more effective, than the conventional use of a reference tool.

- For written communication, what used to require long, handwritten notes on expensive paper now takes a few seconds and happens on the screen of a computer. The new, fast pace of back-to-back communication has already affected our language, which has been compressed and made more efficient.

- Digital text, rather than written text, can be a flexible way to augment communication in its different channels enabled by the Internet.

- Social networks are a new way to approach an old problem—namely, how to democratize information, culture, and communication. In a social network, the virtual and real worlds coexist and often overlap. The consequences of this are quite remarkable and are unfolding daily.

The Future of Communication

- The development of the Internet is so recent that its potential is unfolding constantly, with new unpredicted and unforeseen applications appearing nearly every day.

- Some believe that the future holds a major convergence of devices, creating a single portable device that handles computing, communications, scheduling, and finances—among many other things.

- Another possibility is that computing and communication technology will become so cheap that it's simply embedded into everything, from our appliances to our clothing, and every object will join into an organically linked network.

- Importantly, we will seek a seamless integration of machines and our minds to allow for a more natural way to communicate, but the main challenge—and possibly the greatest accomplishment in the future of communication—is in developing effective ways of organizing communication.

- For the most part, telephones, televisions, and the Internet rely on electromagnetic or optical communication. This type of communication relies on the physics of the 1800s.

- As has happened with the discovery of electromagnetism, a new quantum revolution will most likely happen with completely unpredicted opportunities.

Important Terms

broadcasting: The process of transmitting for general use.

language: A human technology that arises from the needs to provide a common ground for communication; an easy way to categorize an abstract concept.

oral communication: The transmission of a message, idea, or emotion by voice alone.

written communication: The type of communication that is recorded, including any form that is written, stamped, or carved on a supporting material.

Suggested Reading

Beebe, Beebe, and Ivy, *Communication*.

Crowley and Heyer, *Communication in History*.

Grant and Meadows, *Communication Technology Update and Fundamentals*.

Questions to Consider

1. What are the 2 main technology breakthroughs that enabled global communication today, and how will they continue to evolve in the future?

2. In the past, the problem with communication was access to information. What will the challenges be in the future?

Science in the Future

Lecture 24

Science and technology are moving at an exciting and truly incredible pace. Hopefully, this course has conveyed a sense of excitement and wonder for both how and how quickly science and technology are making the world a better place—as evidenced by the example of cloaking in this lecture. Our future is filled with enormous promise for the development of radically new technologies to empower humankind, and breakthroughs in the kinds of scientific research we need to do in order to face the biggest global challenges of our time are going to demand collaboration within the scientific community.

Science and Technology

- The exciting part of science is that the world's most pressing problems are solved collaboratively by teams of people and with the rigor of scientific standards. In a world where so many standards and protocols change, it's comforting that the laws of science—the bases upon which researchers make their investigations—are held to stringent standards.

- The pace of change is such that across the globe these ideas can be shared with unprecedented rapidity and breadth, especially through the Internet. Today, science and technology can enable new science and technology more powerfully than ever before.

- It's not just that we can communicate information faster, for example, by putting our papers in scientific journals online. We have also invented completely new ways to think about and share the scientific data itself.

- For example, today there are databases available with information about millions upon millions of materials, and we can use this information in real time to enhance our research, feeding back new results into the database from our experiments or calculations that can be instantly used by others.

- In many ways, idea sharing is the fulcrum of scientific advance. In fact, advances in how we are able to intersect ideas across scientific boundaries could play the single most important role in the future of science and technology.

- Hundreds of years ago, most scientists had very broad knowledge across the key disciplines of physics, chemistry, mathematics, and biology. Boundaries between fields were almost nonexistent.

- Today, because of our dramatically increased knowledge base and the high degree of specialization that goes with it, it is much harder for a single person to work across these boundaries. However, it is precisely at the intersections between disciplines where the most creative ideas and biggest breakthroughs are likely to happen.

- With nearly limitless opportunities, the science of tomorrow will thrive only if scientists in different disciplines can work together creatively. This is what our own inventions to date have enabled, and this is how the next era of scientific discovery and technology will flourish.

Science Fiction and Science Reality

- Science fiction programs such as *Star Trek* and *The Jetsons* are wonderful examples of how the creativity and imagination of human beings just thinking about the possibilities of science and technology can motivate and drive the discoveries necessary to enable them. Likewise, scientific advances often work their way quickly back into the imagination of the next generation of book and movie writers.

- Of course, just because something is imagined doesn't mean that some day it will turn into a technological reality. Sometimes this is because the idea is extremely challenging, pushing far beyond anything remotely possible at the time—such as teleportation.

- Until only 10 years ago, scientists might have dismissed the concept of cloaking, or making oneself invisible, as only fiction and not possible. Recently, however, new materials have been developed that can actually bend light of a certain frequency around them.

- These materials fall into an entirely new class of materials known as metamaterials, which are engineered to have completely different properties than materials found in nature. The idea for using metamaterials in cloaking is that because of these special optical properties, they can alter how objects interact with light, leading to a device that directs the flow of light smoothly around an object.

- Actual cloaking in the visible part of the spectrum has still not been achieved, but such materials are less than 10 years old and have already shown great promise in many different potential technologies.

- Spiderman, who shot large webs out of his hands to stop bad guys, has been an inspiration to science. It turns out that human-made spiderwebs are a fantastic idea. The tensile strength of a spiderweb—that is, how strong it is when you stretch it—is greater than the same weight of steel and 1000% more flexible.

- The detailed structure of spiderwebs, all the way down to the nanoscale, is something that we are only just beginning to understand,

Human-made spiderwebs are a possibility of the future of science.

© Stockbyte/Thinkstock.

and as scientists understand this amazing material, they are also developing ways to make it.

- The number of possible applications would be immense, from bulletproof vests, to artificial tendons, to the cables in a suspension bridge. In addition, compared to current materials, spider silk is incredibly energy efficient and environmentally friendly to make.

- Very recently, researchers have used genetically modified mammals to produce the proteins needed to make this material and coupled that to an artificial microsized machine that mimics the highly specialized way in which the spider weaves its thread.

- Throughout this course, we've seen many other examples of technologies that might be on the horizon, often first envisioned in the context of science fiction. Other ideas, such as time travel, still may not be completely impossible but are much more distant possibilities.

- On the other hand, some of the best-loved technologies we see in science fiction will likely never be possible, usually because of the fact that they violate some fundamental laws of physics. A spaceship traveling at warp speed—that is, faster than the speed of light—violates Einstein's laws of relativity and is one example of this.

- Science fiction and science reality go back and forth, pushing on one another with great force over time. Whether fiction becomes reality or not, this feedback loop between science, technology, and popular culture is a wonderful blend of determination, intelligence, creativity, and imagination that helps drive future possibilities.

Challenges of Science
- Science is embedded in a society, and as such, it's subject to changes in the political or economic climate. Modern science is an expensive enterprise, and funding it can be a complex endeavor.

- The government funds some of the research going on in the scientific laboratories in our country, but an enormous amount of research is also funded by industry. In many cases, these are companies that don't support basic research themselves, so when they have problems that they cannot address, they pair up with research labs to work on them together.

- In this way, industry gets help addressing its specific research needs, and university scientists get funding for their labs and research activities. Often, the relationship works extremely well, and both groups benefit from exposure to each other's culture.

- However, as more and more science is funded by industry—and, sadly, less and less by government—there's some concern that the interests of industry are not fully aligned with what is required for the broader exploration of science and technology. Naturally, industry will want to focus narrowly on what is beneficial to its specific products and profits.

- Even worse, there have been cases where industry-funded research has utilized scientifically unsound practices in order to provide a biased result that supports the position or product of the company.

- General science is a very tiny fraction of the investment in research by the United States, and as a percentage of the total, it's actually decreased over time. This illustrates a major disconnect between the high expectations of the role of scientists in developing solutions to our most pressing global needs and the low level of importance that is placed on funding science by the government.

- In some cases, science is conducted with a small amount of money that covers personnel and basic laboratory equipment and supplies. In other cases, it may involve the use of a fairly expensive piece of equipment such as a transition electron microscope, which costs a few million dollars.

- Furthermore, there are others kinds of science that simply cannot be done by any one research group or standard piece of equipment. In fact, some of the most fundamental questions for which we seek answers, or problems for which we need new technologies, can only be probed by establishing colossal projects.

- The developments of the atomic bomb under the Manhattan Project and of radar technology at the MIT Radiation Laboratory during World War II, as well as the invention of the transistor at Bell Laboratories in the 1950s, are great examples of how exceptionally rapid technological breakthroughs are possible with large teams working together.

- The paths of scientific discovery and technological need in such large programs inform each other: Advances in basic sciences create entirely new technology possibilities, and likewise, technology-development efforts identify key roadblocks that require improved scientific understanding or completely new approaches.

- Additionally, there are many features of academia that seem at first appealing to aspiring young scientists—such as job security, flexibility to work on different problems, a chance to teach the next generation of talent, and the opportunity to tackle the great problems of our time—but the truth is that the path is long, slow, and hard.

- In addition, the pay is low compared to other professions, and given the other opportunities for bright young minds to engage in, when they look at what lies ahead, it's becoming increasingly difficult to convince them to stay in a career in science.

The Future of Science and Technology

- Despite all of these challenges facing scientists, the future of science and technology couldn't be more exciting than it is now. This is the time for scientists to step up to the most pressing crises we face. Because science and technology have enabled many destructive human behaviors, it is science and technology that must provide the remedies.

- At times, it may appear that some things are beyond our control, yet what is exciting about science and technology is that through the power of using rational, logic-based investigation—and millennia of scientific knowledge as a base—individuals working separately and collaboratively can address these seemingly intractable problems to come up with solutions.

- Scientists will need to take on this responsibility, perhaps in ways they are not used to or in ways that are even outside of their comfort zone. A big part of this will mean learning how to work across disciplines as never before. More and more, we are recognizing the massive potential for new and creative ideas that form only at these intersections.

- Now is the time to recognize—and act on—the urgent need for scientists to cross all disciplinary boundaries. Without collaboration within the scientific community, understanding, innovation, and even serendipitous discoveries will simply not occur nearly as rapidly as they should.

- We, the scientific community, must take on new responsibilities and set examples for how to work together in new ways. We are the ones who have to reach out to the public in any way we can to explain the crucial role of science. We are the ones who have to care more about getting things done and less about who gets the credit. We are the ones who have to think about how we can make the most impact and then do everything we can to make that impact. The responsibility lies with us.

Suggested Reading

Corn, *Imagining Tomorrow*.

Mirowski, *The Effortless Economy of Science?*

Neal, Smith, and McCormick, *Beyond Sputnik*.

Wilson and Horne, *Where's My Jetpack?*

Questions to Consider

1. How do science fiction and science relate to each other? Give examples.

2. What is the role of science and technology in the world today? What do you think it should be in the future?

Glossary

absorption: The process in which hydrogen is dissociated into hydrogen atoms, and then the hydrogen atoms are incorporated into the atomic framework of the solid.

adsorption: The process in which hydrogen is attached to the surface of a material either as hydrogen molecules or as hydrogen atoms.

ampere: The unit of electric current; 1 amp is equal to the current that flows when a potential difference of 1 volt is placed across a wire with a resistance of 1 ohm.

antimicrobial activity: The act of destroying dangerous bacteria or viruses.

antiviral drug: A drug that fights the infection of a virus.

apoptosis: The programmed cell death that all cells have. Between 50 and 70 billion cells in a human body die every day because of apoptosis.

artificial intelligence (AI): The science and engineering of making intelligent machines. The basic idea behind this is to be able to replicate the capabilities of the human mind.

avatar: A mechanical body for humans to exploit, with its "life" coming from humans. These are virtual cyborgs in the way that all of the body is replaced, but the controlling mind is not.

back-propagation algorithm: In this approach to seeing the future, the model of the stock market is continuously fed with previous performance data, including how wrong the model would have been in the past.

base: One of 4 molecules that attach to the backbone of DNA: adenine, cytosine, guanine, and thymine. When bonding across the strands in the helix, A pairs with T, and C fits with G—and vice versa.

biodiesel: A liquid similar to ethanol that is made from soybean oil or recycled cooking oils, but animal fats, other vegetable oils, and other recycled oils can also be used.

biogas: Sometimes called swamp gas, landfill gas, or digester gas, it is made of 50–80% methane, and the rest is mostly carbon dioxide.

biomarker: In medicine, this is a sensor that tracks the locations of things and is made using fluorescent dyes that are chemically modified to attach to whatever it is that needs to be tracked.

broadcasting: The process of transmitting for general use.

carcinogen: Something that can cause a cell to become cancerous.

catalyst: A chemical that helps reactions go faster or enables them to happen at all.

current: The flow of electric charge (measured in amps).

cyborg: A person with mechanical or electronic parts implanted in his or her body to supplement or improve upon human deficiencies.

data mining: Essentially, this is what our brain does when looking for a solution to a problem, but artificial intelligence can do it in massively parallel mode. This process involves the exploration of vast amounts of data and looking for consistent patterns.

desertification: The process by which land on Earth is changing from farming land to desert, in which there is much less precipitation and, therefore, less available water both above ground and underground.

diamagnetic: Materials that do not have magnetic domains and react to an applied external field with an internal field in the opposite direction.

electroencephalography (EEG): A way to detect the electrical activity of the brain in which measurements of electrical activity can be recorded from the outside of the skull.

electrolysis: A process in which the hydrogen and oxygen in water molecules can be encouraged to split apart using an electric current.

electron microscopy: The act of seeing objects with microscopes that use electrons as the light source.

eukaryote: Mostly multicellular organisms having complex cells that contain a nucleus and other membrane-bound structures. Eukaryotes include animals, plants, protists, and fungi.

exon: A part of the DNA molecule that is responsible for the production of proteins but makes up only about 1.5% of the full DNA molecule.

ferromagnetic: Materials that can be permanently magnetic because of their atomic structure.

fossil fuel: A highly energetic energy source that results from biological material being compressed, turned, and transformed through time, pressure, and temperature.

fuel cell: A device that combines 2 chemicals (typically, hydrogen and oxygen), producing electric current in the process.

gene: The segments of the DNA sequence that have a given function or purpose. The precise sequence of these components in the DNA is crucial because it corresponds to a particular functionality within the resulting organism.

genetically modified food (GMF): A hypothetical way to change food by selecting certain aspects of the DNA itself and modifying the DNA.

genetic algorithm: Essentially, instead of looking at the past, these models are designed and left to evolve to their most natural state. The genetic component has to do with the idea that the strongest scenario will prevail.

genetic engineering: The ability to engineer life by accessing, modifying, and altering pieces of the inner source code of life itself.

genomics: The study of the correlation between the arrangement of the components within DNA molecules and the features of a life form.

language: A human technology that arises from the needs to provide a common ground for communication; an easy way to categorize an abstract concept.

magnet: Very broadly, any material that produces a magnetic field. A magnet is simply an object with 2 poles that are attracted to each other. One of these poles is called the north pole, and the other is called the south pole.

magnetism: The effect of a magnetic field created by a magnet on another material.

modeling: Refers to the development of a mathematical representation of a physical situation.

monocellular: An organism made of just one cell.

nanometer: One billionth of a meter.

nanotechnology: The purposeful engineering of matter at scales of less than 100 nanometers to achieve size-dependent properties and functions.

neuron: A particular kind of cell in the brain that exchanges electric signals.

nowcasting: Accurate weather forecasting in a very short range of time.

nuclear fission The splitting of heavy nuclei to release energy.

nuclear fusion: A nuclear reaction in which light nuclei join to produce a heavier nucleus, releasing energy in the process.

optical computing: In this concept, information travels and is also processed as light, or photons, as opposed to electrons.

optics: The study of light and how light travels through and between materials.

oral communication: The transmission of a message, idea, or emotion by voice alone.

osmosis: The process of balancing concentrations across a membrane.

paramagnetic: Materials that cannot be permanently magnetic because of their atomic structure.

photocatalyst: A material that combines the functions of generating electricity from sunlight and acting as an efficient catalyst to split water into the same material.

photon: A tiny burst of energy that composes light.

plastic: In terms of neuroscience, this is the notion that the brain rewires itself over time, altering the strength of connections between neurons.

power: Energy per time measured in watts; equal to voltage times current.

prediction market: An artificial way to use prediction to alter the outcome of an event.

prokaryote: Bacteria that is much simpler in structure than a eukaryote. These cells have no internal membranes and colonized Earth 2 billion years before eukaryotes existed.

pseudoscience: A myth that is persistent enough to masquerade as science.

quantum computing: A kind of futuristic computing that would allow us to solve existing problems with significantly fewer operations. In this approach, the fundamental unit of information—called a quantum bit, or qubit—is not binary as it is with computers. Instead, it is quaternary in nature, a property that arises as a direct consequence of its adherence to the laws of quantum mechanics, which differ radically from the laws of classical physics.

quantum dot: A tiny chunk of matter. The size range for quantum dots are in the size range of the individual letters of genetic code in DNA.

robot: An electromechanical machine that is guided by a computer or artificial intelligence to perform a variety of tasks, from the most specific to the most general. A robot is programmed to perform a task either repetitively or by its own algorithms.

scientific method: A cyclic process of inquiry based on observations, synthesis, hypothesis, and predictions that lead to more observations.

semiconductor: A type of special material that does not conduct electricity unless excited electrons are present.

simulation: Refers to the procedure of solving the equations that result from model development.

solar cell: A material that takes light and converts it to electricity.

spintronics: Similar to the field of electronics that instead uses magnetism and that hypothetically uses the spin of the electron in place of the charge of the electron to do computing. At the heart of spintronics is the fact that even just a single electron is a magnet, with its very own magnetic north and south poles.

square-cube law: In this law, Galileo described the principle that if you increase the size of an animal, for example, by a factor of 2, then you're increasing its area by a factor of 4 and its volume by a factor of 8.

supercomputer: A computer designed to operate, at least in principle, similarly to a brain that is the fastest type of computer currently used. It may contain hundreds of thousands of processors connected by ultrafast networks.

superconductor: A material that, at sufficiently low temperature, exhibits zero resistance to the flow of electric current. Like diamagnets, they react to an applied external field with an internal field in the opposite direction.

synthetic life: The building of new life forms starting from nonliving substances.

transportation: The act of moving people or things from one place to another place.

ubiquitous computing: A kind of futuristic computing in which computing devices could be so small that they would be deeply embedded in the physical world in products or materials—or even human skin—and spread pervasively throughout our environment like smart grains of sand or dust.

virtual pain: A common phenomenon among recent amputees that is a normal reaction mechanism of the brain as it keeps trying to exchange messages to and from a missing part of the body.

visual acuity: This is what sets the limit of what we can see and what we cannot see.

volt: The unit of electric potential in a circuit; a quantitative measure of the electrical potential energy per unit charge.

watt: A rate of energy use that is measured in joules per second; the main unit of power.

written communication: The type of communication that is recorded, including any form that is written, stamped, or carved on a supporting material.

Bibliography

Aifantis, Katerina E., Stephen A. Hackney, and R. Vasant Kumar. *High Energy Density Lithium Batteries: Materials, Engineering, Applications.* Weinheim: Wiley-VCH, 2010.

Allhoff, Fritz, Patrick Lin, James Moor, John Weckert, and Mihail C. Roco. *Nanoethics: The Ethical and Social Implications of Nanotechnology.* Hoboken, NJ: Wiley-Interscience, 2007.

Bandyopadhyay, Supriyo, and Marc Cahay. *Introduction to Spintronics.* Boca Raton, FL: CRC Press, 2008.

Bear, Mark F., Barry W. Connors, and Michael A. Paradiso. *Neuroscience: Exploring the Brain.* Baltimore, MD: Lippincott Williams & Wilkins, 2006.

Beebe, Steven A., Susan J. Beebe, and Diana K. Ivy. *Communication: Principles for a Lifetime.* 4th ed. Boston: Allyn & Bacon, 2009.

Biskup, Agniesezka, and Nick Derington. *Understanding Viruses with Max Axiom, Super Scientist.* Mankato, MN: Capston Press, 2009.

Blatner, David. *The Flying Book: Everything You've Ever Wondered about Flying on Airplanes.* New York: Walker & Company, 2005.

Brock, David C., ed. *Understanding Moore's Law: Four Decades of Innovation.* Philadelphia: Chemical Heritage Press, 2006.

Brown, Guy. *The Living End: The Future of Death, Aging, and Immortality.* New York: Palgrave Macmillan, 2007.

Buzsaki, Gyorgy. *Rhythms of the Brain.* New York: Oxford University Press, 2006.

Canavari, Maurizio, and Kent D. Olson. *Organic Food: Consumers' Choices and Farmers' Opportunities*. New York: Springer, 2007.

Carey, Stephen S. *A Beginner's Guide to Scientific Method*. 4th ed. Belmont, CA: Wadsworth Publishing, 2011.

Chiras, Dan. *Power from the Sun: A Practical Guide to Solar Electricity*. Philadelphia: New Society Publishers, 2009.

Corn, Joseph J. *Imagining Tomorrow: History, Technology, and the American Future*. Cambridge, MA: MIT Press, 1988.

Croft, William J. *Under the Microscope: A Brief History of Microscopy*. Hackensack, NJ: World Scientific, 2006.

Crowley, Daniel, and Paul Heyer. *Communication in History: Technology, Culture, Society*. Boston: Allyn & Bacon, 2010.

Cummings, Claire Hope. *Uncertain Peril: Genetic Engineering and the Future of Seeds*. Boston: Beacon Press, 2009.

Darling, David. *Teleportation: The Impossible Leap*. Hoboken, NJ: John Wiley & Sons, 2005.

Drexler, K. Eric. *Engines of Creation: The Coming Era of Nanotechnology*. New York: Anchor Press, 1986.

Edwards, Mark. *Green Algae Strategy: End Oil Imports and Engineer Sustainable Food and Fuel*. CreateSpace, 2008.

Ferguson, Charles D. *Nuclear Energy: What Everyone Needs to Know*. New York: Oxford University Press, 2011.

Foster, Lynn E. *Nanotechnology: Science, Innovation, and Opportunity*. Upper Saddle River, NJ: Prentice Hall, 2006.

Franklin, James. *What Science Knows: And How It Knows It*. New York: Encounter Books, 2009.

Freedman, Jeri. *Robots through History*. New York: Rosen Central, 2011.

Garcia-Martinez, Javier, and Ernest J. Moniz. *Nanotechnology for the Energy Challenge*. Weinheim: Wiley-VCH, 2010.

Gardner, Dan. *Future Babble: Why Expert Predictions Are Next to Worthless, and You Can Do Better*. New York: Dutton, 2011.

Grant, August E., and Jennifer H. Meadows. *Communication Technology Update and Fundamentals*. 12th ed. Boston: Focal Press, 2010.

Gratzel, Michael, ed. *Nanotechnology*. Vol. 7, *Light and Energy*. N.p.: John Wiley & Sons Inc, 2011.

Green, Martin A. *Third Generation Photovoltaics: Advanced Solar Energy Conversion* (Springer Series in Photonics). New York: Springer, 2005.

Gupta, Ram B. *Hydrogen Fuel: Production, Transport, and Storage*. Boca Raton, FL: CRC Press, 2008.

Hodgson, Michael. *Basic Essentials: Weather Forecasting*. 3rd ed. Guilford, CT: Falcon Guide, 2007.

Jango-Cohen, Judith. *The History of Food* (Major Inventions through History). Minneapolis: Twenty-First Century Books, 2006.

Joint Research Centre. *Hydrogen Storage: State-of-the-Art and Future Perspective*. Edited by European Commission. N.p.: Dictus Publishing, 2011.

Kleinsmith, Lewis J. *Principles of Cancer Biology*. San Francisco: Pearson Benjamin Cummings, 2006.

Kolata, Gina. *Flu: The Story of the Great Influenza Pandemic of 1918 and the Search for the Virus That Caused It*. New York: Touchstone, 2001.

Komp, Richard J. *Practical Photovoltaics: Electricity from Solar Cells*. 3rd ed., rev. Ann Arbor, MI: Aetec Publications, 2002.

Lay, Maxwell G. *Ways of the World: A History of the World's Roads and of the Vehicles That Used Them*. New Brunswick, NJ: Rutgers University Press, 1992.

Lynn, Paul A. *Electricity from Sunlight: An Introduction to Photovoltaics*. Chichester, West Sussex, UK: Wiley, 2010.

Mahaffey, J. *Atomic Awakening: A New Look at the History and Future of Nuclear Power*. New York: Pegasus Books, 2009.

Matricon, Jean, Georges Waysand, and Charles Glashausser. *The Cold Wars: A History of Superconductivity*. New Brunswick, NJ: Rutgers University Press, 2003.

Milazzo, Paul C. *Unlikely Environmentalists: Congress and Clean Water, 1945–1972*. Lawrence: University Press of Kansas, 2006.

Mirowski, Philip. *The Effortless Economy of Science?* Durham, NC: Duke University Press, 2004.

Mnookin, Seth. *The Panic Virus: A True Story of Medicine, Science, and Fear*. New York: Simon & Schuster, 2011.

Moon, Francis C. *Superconducting Levitation: Applications to Bearings and Magnetic Transportation*. New York: Wiley, 1994.

Morlidge, Steve, and Steve Player. *Future Ready: How to Master Business Forecasting*. Hoboken, NJ: Wiley, 2010.

Murphy, Douglas B. *Fundamentals of Light Microscopy and Electronic Imaging*. New York: Wiley-Liss, 2001.

Nazri, Gholam-Abbas, and Gianfranco Pistoia, eds. *Lithium Batteries: Science and Technology*. New York: Springer, 2009.

Neal, Homer A., Tobin Smith, and Jennifer McCormick. *Beyond Sputnik: U.S. Science Policy in the 21st Century*. Ann Arbor: University of Michigan Press, 2008.

Nestle, Marion. *Food Politics: How the Food Industry Influences Nutrition and Health*. Rev. ed. Berkeley: University of California Press, 2007.

Nicholl, Desmond. *An Introduction to Genetic Engineering*. 3rd ed. New York: Cambridge Press, 2008.

Olshansky, S. Jay, and Bruce A. Carnes. *The Quest for Immortality: Science at the Frontiers of Aging*. New York: W. W. Norton & Company, 2002.

Orrell, David. *The Future of Everything: The Science of Prediction*. New York: Basic Books, 2007.

Pahl, Greg. *Biodiesel: Growing a New Energy Economy*. White River Junction, VT: Chelsea Green, 2005.

Rana, Fazale. *Creating Life in the Lab: How New Discoveries in Synthetic Biology Make a Case for the Creator*. Grand Rapids, MI: Baker Books, 2011.

Regis, Edward. *What Is Life?: Investigating the Nature of Life in the Age of Synthetic Biology*. New York: Farrar, Straus, and Giroux, 2008.

Restak, Richard. *The Secret Life of the Brain*. Washington, DC: Joseph Henry Press, 2001.

Rieffel, Eleanor G., and Wolfgang H. Polak. *Quantum Computing: A Gentle Introduction* (Scientific and Engineering Computation). Cambridge, MA: MIT press, 2011.

Rosillo-Calle, Frank, and Francis X. Johnson, eds. *Food versus Fuel: An Informed Introduction to Biofuels*. New York: Zed Books, 2011.

Russell, Stuart, and Peter Norvig. *Artificial Intelligence: A Modern Approach.* 3rd ed. Upper Saddle River, NJ: Prentice Hall, 2010.

Savage, Nora, Mamadou Diallo, Jeremiah Duncan, Anita Street, and Richard Sustich, eds. *Nanotechnology Applications for Clean Water: Solutions for Improving Water Quality* (Micro and Nano Technologies). Norwich, NY: William Andrew, 2009.

Schlesinger, Henry. *The Battery: How Portable Power Sparked a Technological Revolution.* New York: HarperCollins, 2011.

Scientific American. Understanding Artificial Intelligence (Science Made Accessible). New York: Warner Books, 2002.

Scientific American. Understanding Nanotechnology. New York: Warner Books, 2002.

Scientific American. Understanding Supercomputing. New York: Warner Books, 2003.

Seife, Charles. *Sun in a Bottle: The Strange History of Fusion and the Science of Wishful Thinking.* New York: Viking, 2008.

Shanks, Pete. *Human Genetic Engineering: A Guide for Activists, Skeptics, and the Very Perplexed.* New York: Nation Books, 2005.

Shatkin, Jo Anne. *Nanotechnology: Health and Environmental Risks.* Boca Raton, FL: CRC Press, 2008.

Shinjo, Teruya, ed. *Nanomagnetism and Spintronics.* Oxford, UK: Elsevier Science, 2009.

Shors, Teri. *Understanding Viruses.* Sudbury, MA: Jones and Bartlett Publishers, 2009.

Simon, Seymour. *The Brain: Our Nervous System.* New York: Morrow Junior, 2000.

Singer, P.W. *Wired for War: The Robotics Revolution and Conflict in the 21st Century*. New York: Penguin Press, 2009.

Smith, Geoffrey B., and Claes G. Granqvist. *Green Nanotechnology: Solutions for Sustainability and Energy in the Built Environment*. Boca Raton, FL: CRC Press, 2011.

Soetaert, Wim, and Erik Vandamme, eds. *Biofuels* (Wiley Series in Renewable Resource). Hoboken, NJ: Wiley, 2009.

Sperling, Daniel, and Deborah Gordon. *Two Billion Cars: Driving toward Sustainability*. New York, Oxford University Press, 2009.

Strom, Laura Layton. *From Bugbots to Humanoids: Robotics*. New York: Children's Press, 2008.

Tinkham, Michael. *Introduction to Superconductivity*. 2nd ed. Mineola, NY: Dover Publications, 2004.

Vigil, Kenneth M. *Clean Water: An Introduction to Water Quality and Water Pollution Control*. 2nd ed. Corvallis: Oregon State University Press, 2003.

Weinberg, Robert A. *The Biology of Cancer*. New York: Garland Science, Taylor & Francis, 2007.

Wilson, Daniel H., and Richard Horne. *Where's My Jetpack?: A Guide to the Amazing Science Fiction Future That Never Arrived*. New York: Bloomsbury USA, 2007.

Zeilinger, Anton. *Dance of the Photons: From Einstein to Quantum Teleportation*. New York: Farrar, Straus and Giroux, 2010.

Notes

Notes

Notes

Notes

Notes